MW00649407

"This book transcends the limitations of current practitioners on an extraordinary journey into understa........ ... .l meanings of sexual feeling, fantasy, behavior, and physical experience."

Francine Cournos, *professor of Clinical Psychiatry, Mailman School of Public Health, Columbia University*

"Dr. Marcus's work is one of the most important psychoanalytic contributions to our understanding of human sexuality since Sigmund Freud's *Three Essays on Sexuality*. His highly original application of modern ego psychology illuminates the complexity of the human sexual experience, utilizing and synthesizing concepts from all branches of psychoanalysis. This book is an invaluable resource for psychoanalytically understanding, teaching, and treating human sexuality. This work will be a classic."

Les Fleischer, *associate professor, faculty of Health and Behavioural Sciences, Lakehead University; psychoanalyst, private practice*

"Marcus brilliantly uses Freudian ideas to decode the meaning of psychotic hallucinations and delusions in his book *Psychosis and Near Psychosis*. Marcus now, in another brilliant and revelatory work, turns to an experience equally misunderstood, sexual experience; manifest in symbol, fantasy, or rigid arrangements acted out in reality. He shows how physical sexual experiences and longings carry and express our relationships, personalities, deep concerns, fears, hopes, wishes, traumas, and conflicts. He explains why sexual experiences are so powerful in our lives, how they can get stuck, and how treatment can help."

Norman Doidge, *author of* The Brain That Changes Itself

"This book by a master clinician and educator is an ideal book for learning about human sexuality and its psychodynamics. It is appropriate for all levels of training and education. I will use it in my teaching."

Eileen Kavanaugh, *director, Psychiatric Institute Resident's Clinic; medical director, Psychology Externship, New York State Psychiatric Institute, Columbia University Medical Center*

Modern Ego Psychology and Human Sexual Experience

This text examines human sexuality through psychoanalytic theory and modern ego psychology, which looks at emotional meaning and its organization in symbolic representations of affect as organized by the ego.

It starts with an exploration of how symbolic representations are applied to the sensory experience of the body in human sexuality, both in reality and in fantasy. Next, the author delves into the phenomenon of romance as an important self-state in human growth and development. The book concludes with an examination of fetishes and fetish enactments, followed by a discussion of relevant treatments.

With its original and fulsome insights into the workings of human sexuality, this book will prove vital for psychoanalysts and psychotherapists in training and in practice, as well as all those seeking to understand human sexual experiences in greater depth.

Eric R. Marcus is Professor of Clinical Psychiatry and Supervising and Training Psychoanalyst at Columbia University Center for Psychoanalytic Training and Research.

Modern Ego Psychology and Human Sexual Experience

The Meaning of Treatment

Eric R. Marcus

Routledge
Taylor & Francis Group

NEW YORK AND LONDON

Cover image: Four figures etching, by Gerald Marcus

First published 2023
by Routledge
605 Third Avenue, New York, NY 10158

and by Routledge
4 Park Square, Milton Park, Abingdon, Oxon, OX14 4RN

Routledge is an imprint of the Taylor & Francis Group, an informa business

© 2023 Taylor & Francis

Library of Congress Cataloging-in-Publication Data
A catalog record for this title has been requested

ISBN: 978-1-138-58929-2 (hbk)
ISBN: 978-1-138-58930-8 (pbk)
ISBN: 978-0-429-49173-3 (ebk)

DOI: 10.4324/9780429491733

Typeset in Garamond
by Apex CoVantage, LLC

Nihil est in imaginatione quod non fuerit in sensu – nothing is in imagination except that which is in sensation.

Peripatetic axiom found in Thomas Aquinas's *De veritate*,
q. 2 a. 3 arg. 19. (Wikipedia)

Contents

Preface

This book is meant to fill a void in both the sexology and the psychoanalytic literature. The void has to do with the lack of detail about sexual experience and its emotional meaning. Even when there are descriptions of sexual behavior, there are rarely descriptions of the experience of that behavior, and even more rarely, descriptions of the meaning of the experience.

What has psychoanalysis to offer to sexology? It offers a technique for revealing the emotional meaning of sex to an individual. It reveals the emotional contents of sexual desires, fantasies, behaviors and avoidances. It reveals its growth and development sequence and relationships to growth and development of the personality. It shows how inextricably entangled with personality sexual desire, fears, fantasies and behaviors are. It is a method of clinical inquiry and as such reveals the individual meanings, not the so-called normative. It is a clinical method to help an individual; it is not an epidemiology. There can be, however, an epidemiology of sexual fantasy and of meaning. That is a psychodynamic social science issue.

What are some of the possible reasons descriptions of sexual experience and associated meanings are missing from the sexology literature?

One reason, perhaps, is that after the sexual revolution of the 1960s, everything became normal, but then also sex was just sex – anything, anywhere, with anyone, any time, like a sport – and specific meaning, even the deeper meaning of sport, was ignored. This was a political ideology, not a scientific accuracy. It was part of the liberation of women, and of human sexuality, a contribution of science that produced the birth control pill in 1964, and of the post–World War II baby boom generation bulge. Suddenly, there was a population bulge of emerging adults with their intense sexual drives and their yearning to take their place as movers and shakers in the adult world. Older teenagers and very young adults have little adult currency except their adult sexual bodies. Sex therefore became a political statement. It became part of a rebellion catalyzed by these demographics and the political times, the political awakening against the Vietnam War. Sex became a rebellion and a liberation. Make love not war.

At the same time, from the 1950s with Kinsey to the 1960s with Masters and Johnson, sex studies begin to reveal the ubiquity and physiology of sex. But a subtle prejudice remained. Normal became defined by common. Abnormal became defined by uncommon. This was no advance beyond the contributions of the sexual reports of sexual pathologies of the late 1800s of Krafft-Ebing and early 1900s of Havelock Ellis. They were called pathologies because they were assumed to be uncommon and, more importantly, because they did not lead directly to procreation possibility. There are the graphic descriptions of sexual acts and their categories into the various so-called perversions. Those descriptions, while accurate, often were sparse in the details of the sexual activities and almost absent in the description of the experience and emotional meaning of the sexual acts and their details.

Sexual behavior often enacts sexual fantasy. No matter how close the content of the activity, the behavior is never able to fully express the fantasy. In fantasy one can find emotional meaning.

During the 20th century, psychological and social science grew more quantitative, so sex studies emerged whose task was to quantify frequencies of sexual acts. An epidemiology of sexual behavior emerged. Frequency then got enshrined in a condensation with normative, perhaps leading to the assumption of normal and pathological categories.

The problem with normal is its definition. If it is a frequency definition, then uncommon becomes pathological and common becomes normal. Normative becomes normal. This is simply not true. It certainly isn't always true. During the mid-20th century, cigarette smoking was widespread and considered normal. Therefore, one of the most common incidental findings at autopsy was carbonated lungs. Instead of pink, they were black. Nobody claimed that was normal. The proof of abnormality therefore shifted from frequency to pathology. There was a higher rate of lung cancer and chronic obstructive pulmonary disease in smokers. But there were clear markers in the carbon in the lungs and the frequency of disease. Therefore, the label normal at autopsy was changed to the word incidental. But what was incidental for one person was fatal for another; what was incidental for most, was fatal to some.

Because it is hard to establish such pathological markers for human sexuality, it makes the defining of normal difficult and contested. Any attempt to define normal in human sexuality, except at the extremes of damaging behavior, runs into subtle and not-so-subtle value systems. But what is wrong and disgusting to one person or one group, may be exciting and enticing to others.

It is a characteristic of human sexual experience to exist on a spectrum. All categories within that spectrum are also on a continuum. This should be no surprise. Human biology and, even more so, human psychology are complex systems on multiple continuums, with fuzzy boundaries.

In addition, the measurement of normal and abnormal, common and uncommon, for psychoanalysts is riddled with the problem of meaning. For a psychoanalyst it isn't just behavior but rather the meaning of the behavior and the meaning of the meaning. This cannot be found through observation nor reports of the behavior itself. For that we need the fantasy that reveals the emotional story of meaning about sexual behavior. Because there were very few social scientists who were also analysts, we don't get the epidemiology of sexual fantasy. One of the first and only was by Person and Goldberg, both psychoanalysts. Theirs was a study of behavior and fantasy of college students. It was a social science self-report survey done by psychoanalysts. It produced frequencies of both behaviors and fantasies, correlated the two and gave frequencies of enactment of fantasy versus frequency of fantasy only. This is very interesting work, but it does not avoid the problem of normative versus normal, and it does not avoid the problem of surveys in social science research. The data you get from self-report surveys are the data that is produced by the method. The resulting data is about how people answered that survey. It tells you nothing about the correlation of the survey results with actual lived experience, either in behavior or fantasy.

Surveys are questions handed out to a group of people who reply to them, usually with yes or no answers. They are self-reports. So there are now two issues. The first is that the categories tend to be occurrence categories – "Do you or don't you and how often." They tend to eliminate the "neither do nor don't," and the "encourage another to do to you." More importantly, they eliminate qualitative experience as well as meaning.

In addition, the accuracy of such data is notoriously bad. There are two reasons. The first is that shame operates even in anonymity. The second is that denial operates as well. So they don't really tell the surveyor nor themselves. The behaviors and frequencies revealed are therefore reported frequencies whose relationship to actual behavior and frequencies is unknown.

But even assuming they are accurate, they are still based on the assumption that frequency will tell us something interesting other than frequency. And frequency is interesting. But its meaning and significance is not thereby frequently revealed. Something very important, even crucial, to a person may be rare. Something boring and not too meaningful may be frequent.

Human sex studies therefore went from phenomenology to surveys, from individual behavior to group behavior, from descriptions to categories, from the said to be uncommon to the said to be pathological, and from secret to public. All these changes in the growth and development of sexology have tended to minimize meaning and the descriptions of qualitative experience where an important part of meaning can be found.

More recent sexology surveys have been much more sophisticated by including more natural groups and by the sophisticated questions asked. They are revealing the much more common frequency of variations among both men and women than was previously thought. Interestingly, Freud said this. The recent studies are more sophisticated also about unmeasured confounders and accurate data gathering.

The turn of the 19th-century writer who did not pathologize, although accused of so doing, was Sigmund Freud. His book on human sexual experience was ahead of its time in its acceptance of non-pathological sexual variety. It is a lesson that many practitioners of psychoanalysis lost for a number of years in the mid-20th century.

This book makes no claim to knowing what normal is. It is probably best used as a fuzzy concept. It might be good to include in its definition what is good for the growth and development of the self and others and of relationships. Is that a biology imperative or a human values imperative, or both?

One thing that stands in the way of more satisfying relationships is the fear in the sexual self that the sexual other will not enjoy the sexual self, nor what the sexual self wants to do and why. But when two people are intensely attracted to each other, their sexual fantasy experience may be linked; concomitant or concordant.

Another problem in relationships is that the sexual self may know what they want to do but not really why they want to do it, other than lustful satisfaction. The intense, driven meaning is mostly unconscious. Shame and guilt, denial and repression, may make the availability of this information difficult. In fact, one of the pleasures of the deepening of relationships is the exploratory discovery of each with the other, including of their sexual desires.

Another reason perhaps that sexual experience is not in the forefront in modern sexology is the emergence of and focus on the issues of sexual identity and gender. These are the new issues in sexology. They are important issues about which knowledge has accumulated and much more needs to be understood. But no matter the gender, no matter the sexual identity, all human beings have sexual experience and associated sexual fantasy. Sexual fantasy is lacking in the literature about gender and sexual identity.

This book makes no claim to adding some unique contribution to sexology. It means only to call attention to the added phenomenology of meaning, emotional meaning, of sexual experiences and how it is experienced. Fantasy as purveyor of meaning has been known from the dawn of history, elaborated by Freud, but then forgotten in the social sciences, and is in the process of being rediscovered. This is the path of the growth and development of ideas. It follows the approximate Hegelian progression of thesis, antithesis and synthesis. Psychoanalytic theory is in a beginning synthesis phase of its own development and may add to synthesis in allied disciplines.

Fantasy is crucial to psychoanalysis because emotional meaning is therein experienced and expressed. Meaning is revealed more in the fantasy than behavior. Fantasy is a mediator of behavior, a motivator of behavior, but also, crucially, the experience of emotional meaning.

The problem is that much of fantasy is not conscious, or not fully conscious. When fantasy becomes intense, it becomes partially conscious. And there is the opportunity for the analysis of sexual experience. The conscious experience can lead to the unconscious fantasy.

There are fantasies that are common in a group and that can involve the politics of the acceptable in the historical moment. But fantasy is most importantly individual. It follows emotional rules of organization. It is multi-determined and overdetermined. It reveals the unique growth and development pathways and influences that make us, and reveals us as, the unique individuals we are.

The reason we should focus on sexual experience and its details is because emotional meaning, organized as fantasy about the sexual details, helps us to know ourselves and others. All fantasy tends to follow Freud's rules of the organization of emotional concepts, which he called the primary process. Central to the fantasy organization is the putting together, called condensation in the displacement to the details in the fantasy. For sexual fantasy and sexual experience, the details are the qualities of the sexual experience in the experience of the sexual body, self and other. Because sex is not static but rather an enactment over time, the details of the sequence will also contain the condensations of emotional meaning.

There is another reason, perhaps, that sexual details are scarce in psychoanalytic writing. It is because analysts are interested in emotional meaning, but emotional meaning that is unconscious is revealed through associations, and sexual experience may have limited or no associations.

The reasons for this usually understood by analysts are repression due to shame and guilt. But there is another reason. This has to do with the intensity of the lust affect experience. Lust is so intense, such a reward in and of itself, so linked to the specific anatomic and physiologic details of the body, conveyed through the sensory system, that it seems as if it is only what it is – just a property of the sexual object and the sexual activity. It is exciting. It is fun. Or it is fun and anxious. Or it is fun and guilty and shameful. But it is what it is. That is all that it is. Guilt and shame seem reactions to it rather than part of it. It is what it is may be a major resistance to the discovery of meaning both in the patient and perhaps in the analyst.

The error that analysts may make is to seek only associations to the behavior rather than first a detailed description of the qualities of the experience and then the meaning of those qualities, to be found in the associations to the experience of the details. This is the meaning the details represent and express. Thus is the inherent fantasy revealed. When you get only associations to the behavior, you get the attitude about the fantasy, not the fantasy. Both are interesting. But the second is crucial. It is the core.

The crucial beginning of meaning of sexual experience is to be found in the sexual experience. Behavior and qualities of experience are condensed with emotional meaning. Attraction is meaning. Qualities are mediating and express emotional fantasy. The marvelous qualitative sensory human brain is being harnessed as an information pathway for symbolic representation using the intense affect of lust.

So submerged is sexual meaning in the sexual action, that patients may say their experience would be true for anybody, a property of the sexual object and the sexual action. The answer is maybe yes, maybe no, but it has special meaning to the self, and the question is, what is that special meaning. The goal is to help the patient understand that sex in the sexual object or things in themselves are arousing as sensory stimuli but the arousal and the meaning are in the patient's emotional self.

Because the analyst is also human, we are subject to sexual arousal and lust affect. We are therefore vulnerable also to reactions against and resistance to the sexual fantasy that lust triggers in us and that organizes our lust experience.

Our own unconscious neurosis may prevent the elicitation or elaboration or contemplation of significance or empathic reception of sexual material by the patient. While a hindrance, this can also be a growth and development pathway for the analyst over the course of a career. The observation of self-resistance can lead to the self-analysis of sexual fantasy scrupulosity. The opportunity for self-analysis and self-care, in parallel with care of the patient, is another reason for this book.

This book may help general psychiatry in its goal of the categorization of sexual pathology. Psychiatry has made considerable progress in the expanding of its categories. It must now relax its definitions so that categories are continuums and not rigidly boundaried. Rigid boundaries trap, and exclude, even as they specify. Data then gets sorted a priori. Categories rather should emerge from observational data. Psychoanalysis of the individual has to give to psychiatric diagnosis and epidemiology, the two concepts of individuals on a continuum and the qualitative as data, not just quantities of occurrences. Taken into account, these two most human features will make general psychiatry and its epidemiology more accurate and more useful.

For psychoanalysis, the book helps to contribute to phenomenology, treatment and theory. These three are linked. They are linked as well to a fourth, which is empathic attitude. Psychoanalysts are interested in the emotional, in the unconscious emotional, and therefore the analytic phenomenology must include, if not center on, that. Accurate treatment depends on it. It will help empathic attitude. It will also help theory, because in psychoanalysis, theory is about clinical theory of mind. Clinical theory of mind is about the phenomena of human experience, including emotional meaning. Lack of accurate information about qualitative experience and associated fantasy limits the objective observational clinical science that psychoanalysis strives to be.

This is where modern ego psychology comes in. Embracing observational experience of the human mind, trying to describe it accurately in its complexity, conscious, preconscious, unconscious, modern ego psychology tries through accurate and complex description to develop a general psychology including all aspects of the human mind: the emotional, the cognitive, the sensory, and the relationships among them. This branch of psychology theory takes as its epistemological base, objective phenomenology. It therefore strives to describe our observations of what we categorize as reality experience and therefore by implication only, but importantly, the real world. It then takes the crucial step of including the observation of mental phenomena as an aspect of the natural world. Because of the nature of mind, the theory takes another step to include the qualitative under the purview of objective phenomenology. Then it takes the next step of including the description of mental qualities in the science of mind. Importantly, the science of qualities is more akin to social science than to physical science. Social science in the 20th century shifted to quantitative science but has rediscovered qualitative science in the 21st century.

Interestingly, one can quantify qualities. One can run certain mathematical and statistical operations on them. But in order to usefully do so, they must be counted without diminishing or changing the qualitative information. This requires a technique of science wherein the categories emerge from the data. Categories are not a priori imposed. If you do so, you will eliminate that which is most important to be counted, the individual qualities. Therefore care must be taken to preserve the original qualitative meanings. Otherwise you are counting the counting and not the phenomena.

One must also be careful about the purpose to which the counting is put. For some purposes, counting is appropriate. For other purposes, counting is both useless and misleading. The story of meaning is an emotional narrative, a story, not just a sequence of event occurrences. Different narratives or similar narratives from different people may have similar elements and similar meanings the quantifying can help clarify, but, ultimately, for each individual, the meaning is unique.

The book is also intended as an illustration of intense emotional qualitative experience called thing presentation phenomena and experience. Thing presentations are sensory-emotional experiences, both at once, that illustrate as we experience. The meaning of what we experience is illustrated in what we experience. They are a basic aspect of human mental function. They are an important information highway. They are an important aspect of creativity. They present themselves to the mind preformed as an "aha" experience. They play a role in all creativity, from poetry to science, from Yeats to Einstein. They are an experience of a thing in itself. The mythical Kantian "das ding." It was first described as a neuro-mental phenomena by Freud. They are consciously apparent in dreams, in delusions and hallucinations, in art and, now the point, in sexual experience. It seems as though the qualities of meaning are inherent in the physicality of the thing. This is why it will be hard to analyze, because the patient experiences it as an other. The experience is therefore of an arousing body part, arousing because of the body part, not because of the meaning of the body part to the person aroused. Therefore, it seems as though there's nothing to talk about except the qualities of the body part. It is the analytic task to focus on that experience, the qualities of the body part, qualities of action on the body part, because in the experience is condensed the emotional meaning. The place to look is in the qualities of the body part as experienced in the patient's sensory emotional system. Just like a dream.

This book is primarily intended for teaching. Used for information and description of phenomenology, it can then lead to the discussions that help work through the material so that the beginning analyst and therapist can approach sexually charged patient reports and use them to help.

An immediate problem in teaching is either the avoidance of or provocation by explicit sexual material, particularly in those just starting out. Because it is exciting and arousing, the young therapist and analyst immediately worry that it is wrong for the therapist and analyst to feel it. Reassurance about countertransference doesn't quite work because they don't experience it as countertransference. They experience as independent arousal to listening to sexually arousing material. It is like porn. This feels like voyeurism. It doesn't feel as though it is in response to the patient but rather an independent reaction in the student analyst. This is true, but it also involves the countertransference fantasy to sexual material itself that frequently troubles the beginner. It may be more troubling to the non-physician who hasn't already had to wrestle with the emotional evocation and burden of nakedness, exposure, intrusive physical procedures, patient reactions and physician counterreactions. Having come to some equilibrium with that, the sexual material is actually less of a challenge, although not easy. But the challenge for them is that medical training teaches the suppression and repression of emotional response to the physical. So the physician can tolerate the material but not the fantasies that it provokes. The non-physician analyst or therapist may be overwhelmed by the actual sexual descriptions and the fantasies it provokes.

The next is the beginner's unconscious assumption of normative. Often they think, without full awareness, that they know what is normal. Like the famous supreme court justice, they know abnormal when they see it. They may have been taught in medical school and graduate school about sex surveys and what epidemiology shows to be normative. The normative is then taken without sophisticated explanation as equivalent to normal. On the other hand, the young may say that sex is just sex and anything goes and why go deeper because there isn't any deeper. But that, of course, is a fantasy of its own. It's a fantasy about sport fucking. It's a fantasy that sex is what it is and is all that it is. To the experienced analyst, that's OK because that is actually a fantasy about sex and an experience of sex. Sport has deep meanings. It has its own object relations. It's the object relations of a sport, somewhat competitive, somewhat mutual, give to get and get to give, transactional, with the goal of orgasm and no intimacy or permanence implied. This can be true for both parties. Web apps have made the sport an easily available hobby. But it has that deeper transactional meaning, and the meaning of that meaning.

Now can be the time to teach growth and development of psychology, with a focus on emerging adult challenges of linking sex and intimacy. This will introduce the growth and development trajectory of object relations in human relationships, and the lines of development of ego functions and ego processes that organize, enclose, condense, symbolize and integrate object relations. These processes are so well illustrated by the growth and development of sexual experience.

It is also a good time to teach empathic holding, because lustful excitement can disrupt the taking in, the experience of, the associations to and the contemplations about patient experience. It gives a chance to discuss what empathic holding is, in all its complexity and attitudinal requirements, as well as some of its disruptors and defenses. It is this complicated process that is basic to psychoanalysis and to psychodynamic psychotherapy. Lustful excitement is often a greater disruptor then patient rage.

Both are the challenges of tolerating affect intensity and associated evoked fantasies and perhaps painful conflict of memories. The patient may be a step ahead of the analyst in the toleration of the lustful fantasy. This is because the analyst has worked hard on the defenses against it in the patient but not necessarily in themself. Particularly if the sexual material touches on and evokes sexual fantasy that is in neurotic conflict within the analyst, then the difficulty can be intense. But it also offers the opportunity for self-analysis, or within their therapeutic analysis if that is going on for the therapist. Either way, the experience of listening to and therapeutically holding intense sexual fantasy offers the opportunity for growth and development in both parties of the therapeutic alliance as it potentially does with any two people in their everyday sexual life with each other.

This book can also be used to teach and discuss technique, both in general and specifically with sexual behavior and fantasy. It is all the same technique with different degrees of difficulty because of different degrees of resistance in the patient and in the analyst, depending on the content of the fantasy of which sexual fantasy is one of the most intense and the most triggering of guilt and shame.

One problem that authors of books like this have is the claim of their colleagues that examples are all made up by the author and show their proclivities not patients. This accusation is particularly from analysts who have not been able to elicit such fantasy material in their patients. The accusation is logically a bit irrelevant because even if it's true, the made up is also a revelation of sexual fantasy and the only question is its accuracy and applicability to patients. Masud Khan is thusly accused, but I have found his descriptions very consistent with patient reports. If he made them up, was talking about his own fantasies, he reported them accurately, perhaps based on his experience not only of himself but of his patients. In any case, because of privacy considerations, the analyst must disguise and thereby change, thus to contaminate and create. It is inevitable. But again, this is always the problem even in the consulting room, listening to intense sexual material. Better to read and learn then reject and attack.

The other worry that analysts have about human sexuality in the consulting room is the fear of boundary crossing where analyst and patient become sexually involved with each other in reality behavior. This is an important and real worry. It is one of the burdens placed upon us and requires us to mentally lash ourselves to our chairs as we pass the sirens of desire, like brave Odysseus. By doing the work, we accept this challenge; to experience fantasy mentally yet keep it separate from action. But this is a daily struggle in all human beings about many different emotions and fantasies. It is very hard if vulnerable in our own lives. It is why psychoanalytic treatment is not only helpful but probably mandatory for anyone who wants to do this work. It is obviously helpful if the analyst's own therapeutic analysis includes sexual behavior and sexual fantasy. If it does not, what chance will there be for it to be explored safely or at all with patients. Granted those who can't do teach, but, in this case, treating a patient is not only teaching but doing. The problem is to feel but not to do; to contain the doing to fantasy.

A problem of pedagogy is when a course on human sexuality involves a grade. This adds a burden of resistance to the discussion because the student may feel they will be graded on their normalcy. This is a particular problem if they have more unconscious guilt and shame than they realize. The burden will be placed on the teacher to discuss this openly and create a pedagogical attitude and learning environment that can receive sexual information and discuss it.

One boundary that is useful is the boundary against too much self-disclosure in the classroom by the students. This is what is frightening for them. They will usually regulate it as tolerated by them, especially if they are not expected to be, nor are called upon to be, revelatory. They can sometimes be more revelatory than they realize in their discussion but it then behooves the teacher never to interpret them. The focus is on the patient's material and what is evoked by the patient's material, and is therefore relevant to the patient not the student. Of course, this does not preclude, but even more so requires, a discussion of guilt and shame in relationship to sexual fantasy. Students nowadays, can be quite comfortable with sexual activity in all its varieties but the teacher should not make the mistake of thinking that means they are comfortable with sexual fantasy, neither the patient's nor especially, perhaps, their own.

The savvy teacher will allow the class to regulate the depth of their discussion. If they are having trouble, general comments about the class can safely be made. Individual interpretive comments are to be very much avoided. They are there in a learning environment not in a therapeutic environment. The temptation to cross that boundary may be intense in the teacher because that can be sexually exciting. But avoiding it is a demonstration of the proper use of boundary function. This boundary function is in service to the student, just as in the office it is in service to the patient's growth and development. If we deliver early interpretations, in the classroom or in the office, we will receive aggressive resistance, as well we should. You will now be teaching the opposite of what you intended. Remember that how you teach is also what you teach. When you teach you are teaching an attitude not just content. You are teaching your attitude to the content and task.

Teach with an attitude of concern for students and patients, and of love for your topic. We teach mastery but this should not be for a narcissistic demonstration of mastery. The teacher should have the authority of their knowledge and experience. Any attempt to use the power differential is an error and reflects on the teacher's insecurity. The secure teacher understands that knowledge is the only necessary power a teacher should bring to class.

This book is in the context of a point of view, a theory of psychoanalysis called modern ego psychology. I's goal is not to further the development of that theory, which I have tried to do elsewhere, but to illustrate it and to show and teach its use for understanding and for treatment technique. It is not meant to replace any other theory but rather to integrate theory since it looks at complicated mental experience, including all the subdivisions of conflict, object relations, interpersonal relations, intersubjectivity, self and reality adaptation. All of mental experience. This includes cognition. Includes the conscious and preconscious as well as the unconscious. It particularly focuses on affect-organized and synthesized symbolic representations of all this mental experience. Sexual experience is illustrative of this because it includes all of these elements. The book will illustrate each aspect as well as a synthetic capacity inherent in symbolic alterations of reality, specifically, lustful symbolic alterations of the body. The synthesis is in the symbolic representation which condenses a synthesis that it illustrates. Its synthesis is not conscious. But once it becomes conscious as a mental experience, it can be used by the secondary process of logic and the tertiary process of re-synthesis to achieve a real-world use of the information contained in the symbolic representation. It is based on emotional meaning. Emotional meaning isn't just about emotions but about emotional significance, and that points us not only to our unconscious but to reality. It helps us understand what reality means to us and therefore what changes we might want to make. These changes will further emotional satisfaction. Since adaptation to reality gives emotional satisfaction, the tertiary process use of symbolic representation will bring better reality adaptation. Because synthesis and adaptation are ego functions, it is perhaps modern ego psychology that has the specificity of observations about ego function, therefore to contribute in this way.

It is hoped that this book will help those who read it to further this goal for themselves and actualize their satisfaction in their treatments and in their own sexual relationships as a vehicle to growth and development.

Introduction

This is a book about the meaning in human sexual experience. It will be used to describe treatment with psychoanalysis or psychodynamic psychotherapy. To the psychoanalyst and to the patient, this means engaging in an emotional meaning experience.

Sex is more than physical pleasure. It is emotional pleasure. Sex is more than physical release. It is also emotional satisfaction. This is a book about how to understand the emotional satisfaction of physical sexual experience unique to each individual.

The book focuses on the physical experience of sex. The physical can express and satisfy the emotional because the physical experience is representing and expressing the emotional experience. Physical sexual experience can be a symbolic representation of emotional meaning. Therefore, what this book is about is how human sexual-emotional meaning is experientially encoded in symbolic representation experiences of sex. The book will show the psychological meaning in the sensuous details of sexual experience. This book will show the emotional meaning in the mental representation experience of the physical. It will help therapists help people understand their sexual experience in order to understand their conflicts and increase their emotional fulfillment in sex and in relationships.

Understanding sexual symbolic representations, their organizations and uses, will allow a description of the sexual pathologies in terms of their emotional meanings and emotional functions rather than just their behaviors.

The actual human experience of sexuality is often missing from the psychoanalytic literature, which replaces it with the descriptive theories of motivation, of conflict, of object relations imposed upon sexual experience rather than growing from it. This has left out the particular qualities and intensities of sexual experience and their emotional meanings. The structures of the physicality of sexual experience is an important aspect of what clinical theories of mind should describe.

Sex is an enactment modality for modeling emotional meaning in physical sensory metaphors. There are many different emotional feelings and paradigms. They range from love to beauty, to joy, to love, to bonding, to power,

DOI: 10.4324/9780429491733-1

DOI: 10.4324/9780429491733-1

to dominance, to control, to attachment, to independence. The psychoanalytic contribution adds that some or all of these at the same time, in conflict, form sexual emotional representations in the mind resulting in representations of compromises of meanings; an attempt at synthesis.

This book is about those meanings and how to discover them. The book is about how they are constructed and their resulting structure. This book is needed because without basic descriptions of the physical experiences and their meanings, doing therapy may become superficial and avoidant. The patient's involvement is with the particular sensory emotional experience of the aroused human body that human sexuality is. This book will show how some of the crucial and most meaningful emotional dynamics are contained within those sensory emotional experiences. Then it won't be about the what and the where of sexual activity. It will be about the who and the why.

I do not mean to proscribe or even prescribe. I mean to describe. Understood is that each human is unique. Any one person may fit some of these descriptions or none.

Any examples I give are heavily disguised or fabricated from what I have heard over many years. Resemblance to anyone is coincidental. How granular to be in the examples? To fail to do that does not properly illustrate. But the danger is if too evocative or provocative, it may shift the reading and even the audience to the salacious enjoyment of the examples rather than the concepts in the book and the examples as illustrations of concepts. But to leave out the details, as most psychoanalytic writing does, is to leave out crucial meanings. This book tries for balance.

This is a teaching book. The bibliography is for background not specific scholarly citation. These are some of the books wherein many of the these ideas can be found. This book focuses on the sensory experience of sex and the ego functions that organize it. This is perhaps its only original idea and even that is just an emphasis and application of Freud's original idea of thing presentation and of ego function.

In sexual sensory experience are important dynamics. The definitions, the dynamics, have been in the sex literature for many, many years. But the specific focus on the sensory experience has been strangely minimal. It may be another example of the power of the sexual sensory experience to trigger shame and humiliation reactions because the excitement cannot be hidden from the self.

This book uses modern ego psychology and focuses on affect representations: their structures and organizations, their modalities and phenomenology, and their ego processes and organizing spectrums. To understand these structures and processes of sexual representations is to understand the deeper meanings that are included in these structures.

Not everyone experiences sex so intensely and so meaningfully. This book describes those who do.

Chapter 1

Meaning

Psychoanalysis is ultimately a science of meaning and of the art of meaning making. It achieves understanding by carefully listening and eliciting patient experiences, especially the experience of meaning. In psychoanalysis, meaning is emotional meaning, called affect meaning and associated affect ideas. Its regularities are called structure. They are composed of units of meaning. All of these units of meaning have in common the tendency to become stable structures of meaning. Is there a universal unit? The micro unit for modern ego psychology is symbolic representations of emotional meaning, a multisensory pictogram experience to be described. It is how affect meaning is represented in mental experience. The macro units are agencies of the self, composed of groups of micro representations serving a common function. The traditional ones are id, superego and ego, for drives, conscience and the executive functions of internal regulations and adaptations. The largest macro unit is the organized experience of all units. This integrated, synthesized experience is called the self, sometimes called personality or character.

In human sexual experience, meaning is the meaning in the experience, not just the meaning of the experience. Intense sexual meaning experiences therefore have a double meaning – the meaning in the experience and the meaning of the experience. These two may be in conflict. There may be intense sexual excitement meaning when aroused and a deep shame about it when not aroused or even at the same time.

Modern Ego Psychology

The ego is the name Freud gave to the organizing processes of the mind. These processes organize external and internal information modalities. Modern ego psychology adds to psychoanalytic theory the description of the ego's information organizing processes and their effects. These processes organize mental experiences into representations. The organization may differ according to meaning, modalities, intensity, qualities, illness or endowment.

DOI: 10.4324/9780429491733-2

It is the ego that integrates the experience of reality with the experience of the emotions. Therefore, it is these ego processes that attach emotional meaning to experience. The basic unit of mental experience from the ego point of view is the resulting experience of representation and especially symbolic representation that encodes the experience of emotional meaning. The ego processes organize these representations and their uses. Symbolic representations are affect representation – representations of emotional meaning. The ego is the major meaning organizer.

For modern ego psychology, affect is the meaning maker. The self is the experiencer. Perhaps it required a modern ego psychology to look carefully at symbolic representation because it is the ego and its processes that organize affect meaning into nodes of representation and to further organize these representations into a story, which psychoanalysts call fantasy. Fantasy is conscious, preconscious and unconscious. These emotional fantasy stories are experienced and organized by mental processes called ego functions and are major organizers of personality. It is ego functions that organize stories, relationships and the relationship between fantasy and reality. Modern ego psychology is about the stable processes and structures of organized meaning. Human sexual experience is a meaning experience that tends to be a stable structure for each person.

Modalities of Meaning

The mind has different modalities for experiencing meaning. In order to understand human mental experience, it is helpful to understand that information is processed in different modalities and is differently experienced and organized in and among those modalities. Three large general modalities are the language and logic modality, the emotional modality, and the sensory modality. The qualities of experience are different in each of the three modalities. The rules of organization are different in each. There are syntheses in and between all three. These syntheses become their own different combination modalities. The experience of these modalities is part of our experience of meaning and of self.

The language and logic modality is organized by what Freud called the secondary process because he, probably wrongly, believed it developed after emotional processes begin. Secondary processes are of logic and language. They have specific rules in their organization of information. Language and logic tend to organize information distinctly, as facts and event occurrences, clearly boundaried, in sequences, with exact definitions, and with temporality related to cause-and-effect. The discretely boundaried information and categories are a type of digital data and digital processing. The exception to this is metaphor, a special type of language use that refers to emotional thinking and its products. It is therefore a type of translation whose manifest organization is still secondary process in organization. Its representations tend to be in discrete words with multiple referents, often calling indirectly upon the visual, but still a language-based experience.

A different modality psychoanalysts call affect experience. Affect experience is the experience of our emotional feelings. It is a felt experience and only secondarily a thought experience. Emotional feelings are especially important because they give meaning to lived reality experience. Their unique combinations and occurrence tendencies make for unique individuals. Freud called this the primary process. It is analog information. Its informational representations are qualitative. Information is processed according to qualities and quantities on infinite intensity quality gradients and simultaneously as well as sequentially. It organizes all information qualities, quantities, gradients, and processes along continuous spectra, also called dimensionals. It is organized according to emotional meaning. Similar affect will gather together similar affect-related ideas. The product of the primary process is called affect contents.

The sensory system receives and organizes stimuli from the external and internal environments. This, too, is an analog system that does, however, also register discrete digital stimulus events and their categories. This is a crucial system for navigating in the external world and for the sensory oversight of our bodies. It is also particularly good at experiencing qualities and quantities along infinite intensity gradients. Its informational representations are both discrete occurrences and qualitative and analog. Analog means continuous. This makes it an ideal venue for also experiencing emotions, a crucial feature of which is its infinitely varying intensities. The sensory system adds a quality and quantity modality. That humans say they feel their emotions is the reference to the sensory system.

Whenever we have a derivative of unconscious emotional processing, in dreams, in fantasy, in art, we see the use of the sensory modality for representation. Especially the visual system is used but also the tactile, the auditory, the gustatory and the olfactory. This is especially true in human sexual experience. The unconscious that Freud said was a body ego is even more fundamentally a sensory ego because the body is experienced in the sensory system. This is important because it is the capacities and limitations of the sensory system, not the body itself, that gives its qualities to representations, even representations of the physical.

Sensory experience is used to experience emotional states because the body's sensory emotional nexus is primed to do so. Symbolic representations tend to be pictograms. Because in sexual arousal, the sensory and the emotional are simultaneous, the representations of sexual experience tend to be sensory emotional ones. The sensory experience of the self and other's sexual bodies are experienced simultaneously with emotional meaning. Sex is a sensory emotional experience. Understanding the form of this experience will help understand meaning.

Any of these three systems, alone or in combination, can build their experience into an organized representation. Sex tends to be a sensory emotional experience.

Symbolic Representation

Reality is registered in the mind and represented directly as reality, whether strictly veridical or not. It is called a representation. But when psychoanalysts use the term "representation," they usually mean symbolic representation of emotional meaning. Emotions can be felt directly but, if represented, are represented as something. The something is a kind of pictogram portrayal of the affect's concept; the emotional idea. Symbolic representation is a representation especially of the affect meaning. The mental experience of symbolic representation is of a sensory emotional experience. The constructed representation is called a symbolic representation because it refers to a complex, condensed, fuzzy set of emotional meanings contained in the affect concept. It is one form that meaning experiences take.

The structure of symbolic representations represents an emotional idea and its different iterations by combining them together, called condensation, into one image or other sensory manifestation. The affect meanings are organized according to rules Freud described. The first is condensation, the bringing together, resulting in a type of merger, producing a symbol construction made up of and referring to many iterations of an emotional idea. The crucial information processing in the condensed symbol is not the putting together but the displacement to details. Emotional meanings in the condensation are displaced to the details. The affect is displaced to, and experienced in, the experience of the sensory details. The details are the most important aspect in the encoding of affect and its ideas in representations. Reflecting on those details will therefore tend to evoke and reveal the meanings. The experience is felt, not thought. Sensory details of sexual experience are felt and encode the emotional meaning of sex.

Human emotion often involves conflicted feelings. In a symbolic representation, all the elements of conflict may be symbolically represented. The elements of emotional conflict have undergone a creative transformation into a new synthesis with a new meaning. Symbolic representation is the synthesized condensed compromise of the still existing conflicts.

Symbolic representations and their organizations are layered in the conscious, preconscious and unconscious with multi-determined, multifactorial and multimodal constructions. They are organized according to the specific emotional rules of primary process and only when conscious, further organized by secondary and tertiary processes. The symbolic representation allows the simultaneous experience in the primary process of affect organization, the secondary process of logic organization and the tertiary process of the synthesis of both.

The multi-determined and overdetermined condensations form multi-meaning representations, which form metaphors and stories that psychoanalysts call fantasies. They are called fantasies because they are not only constructed of reality experience and emotional experience but also of imaginary experiences; wished-for experiences, feared experiences, and their conflicts and compromises. They are imaginary scenarios and searched-for solutions. Symbolic representations are a note to ourselves about emotional meaning as it relates to ourselves and our experiences of others. They are about our feelings and are also about the emotional meaning to us of reality. Symbolic representations are the glue that organizes and motivates and illustrates human experience of emotional meaning. Object relations are relationships between symbolic representations of self and other. Object relations are therefore a class or category of symbolic representation.

The sum total of symbolic representations is the human experience of meaning that builds over years of time, and with temperament, organized in characteristic style, forms the attitudes of personality.

One of the best examples of this type of structure and of meaning is the dream. Symbolic representations structured in the dream are composed of a reality event or thought called the day residue, which is symbolically altered and experienced in the sensory system. In the dream, the different ways that the mind has of organizing its emotional experience, conflict and compromise, object relations, self, interpersonal exchanges, are all aspects of the organized experience of affect representations and their meanings as experienced in the sensory system of the dream, mostly visual. In human sexual experience, the day residue is the sexual body.

Symbolic representations are composed of all these modalities of information processing, which is the key to the usefulness of these plastic representations. Plasticity is a key to their adaptive use in relationship to reality and in relationship to interpersonal emotional adaptation and to growth and development of the self.

These processes organize symbolic representations into fantasies. Conscious and unconscious, fantasy is a holographic spectrum experience with different forms at different topographic levels. Fantasy is the narrative structure that symbolic representations take to express their meaning story.

Neurotic symbolic representations are stereotyped and not plastic and have captured an area of emotional experience. Near psychotic symbolic representations are stereotyped and have captured an area of reality experience in the preconscious. Psychotic symbolic representations are stereotyped, fixed and have captured an aspect of reality experience in consciousness.

There are many types of categories of symbolic representation. Knowing the different types and their structures will help understand meaning and will help analyze patients. They have special relevance in human sexual experience.

Symbolic Alterations of Realty

Reality experience is based on sensory experience. Emotional experience is an affect experience. A special type of symbolic representation uses reality for emotional experience and makes it, with its alterations, the representation. Then reality experience is more than just the kernel of a day residue. The experience is of reality.

It is the use of altered reality experience as metaphors of emotional meaning; emotional experiences are using reality experience to represent and express. In symbolic alterations of reality, the experience of the properties of reality experience are changed to better represent, express and experience affect contents.

Symbolic alterations of reality are a type of symbolic representation that uses external reality in conscious reality experience for symbolic representation of emotional meaning. Representation attaches the emotional meaning, the emotional significance, to reality experience. It may be attached to a reality form found in reality or it may be a reality form altered, in the mind, for a more specific and accurate representation of affect meaning. Symbolic alterations of reality are affect-altered reality experience. It is reality experience altered to better represent and express emotional meaning.

The most obvious examples are art objects. Portraits often portray the face of a person in their uniqueness as a person, not just their anatomy. Such portraits portray something of how the artist experiences the person. The portrait shows something of how the person feels about themselves. The reality anatomy of the portrait face is therefore changed to express these personality characteristics as perceived by the artist.

How this is done is part of what we call the artist's style. The relationship of this example to everyday life is that each person perceives other people and parts of reality in their own artistic way. Dreams are the most obvious example of our minds ability to construct artistic, mental symbolic alterations of reality.

Symbolic alterations of reality remain plastic. Symbolic alterations of reality provide a venue for continuous projection, introjection and projective identification. Symbolic alterations of reality are a condensation mixture of the real object and the object representation, the real self and the self-representation, in a mixture of wish and fantasy, of mastery and avoidance, of positive and negative reinforcers.

Another important aspect of symbolic alterations of reality is the capacity not just for representation but for discharge and not just of drive but of emotional satisfaction. All motivation of whatever sort seeks change. This is part of the definition of motivation; motivation for what. Representation that is symbolic and particularly that which alters objects in reality or the experience of reality, makes the change aspect of motivation very clear. Even in fantasy, the construction allows for motivational discharge and emotional satisfaction.

This makes symbolic representations potentially transformational of reality and of the self. Secondary and tertiary plasticity of these structures allows for this transformation. Plasticity means changeable and changing. They are creative constructions. It is potentially transformational of reality, guiding us about how we wish to change reality. It is potentially transformational of how we feel, and how we tend to feel, about ourselves, about others and about the world in which we live. You can guide the satisfying and adaptive constructions of reality that humans build, in both the physical and relationship environments. Human sexual behavior is an example of this, because it is used to build a relationship with another human being. Even casual sex implies a relationship to the sexual partner.

Thing Presentations

A special type of symbolic alteration of reality is what Freud called thing presentations. Emotional meaning intensity may activate the sensory system very intensely and if the intensity is strong enough, a sensory representation suddenly appears in the mind, strongly delineated and complete in form and filled with emotional meaning. The meaning is experienced as qualities of the object, not of the self. This is what distinguishes thing presentation experience from other sensory emotional symbolic representations where the self feels the meaning as their own emotional response to the thing rather than just a quality of the thing. In art, the observer has an emotional reaction to the symbolically altered representation of art. In a thing presentation, emotional reaction is seen as a property of the presentation. The emotional reaction is intense enough to condense into a specific, delineated sensory representation. The intense perceptual qualities seem to be inherent in the thing itself, therefore, so does the affect meaning, because both the sensory and the emotional are experienced together, as one.

Thing presentation experiences not only use reality, their meanings are trapped by reality and fixed. Their experience is not of the meaning of reality but rather of reality's meaning. Its meaning seems to be part of its reality. The two, meaning and reality, are experienced together. The sensation and the emotion have condensed together in the sensory system.

The thing presentation definition and experience involves the condensation of exteroceptive sensory experience plus affect experience, both condensed together with and experienced in reality experience. It is a representation of an object in reality, plus our feelings about that object, plus other feelings about ourselves added because of associated meanings, all contained in the representability capacities of the object. The thing presentation experience is a reified sensory emotional meaning experience of the object's qualities perceived as an aspect of the object, not feelings about the object.

The thing part of the term that Freud used refers to the material object and its perception in the exteroceptive sensory system as an external, fixed, emotionally significant but independent thing. The presentation part of the term refers to the experience of it appearing in consciousness fully formed. It doesn't seem to be a construction. It isn't experienced in the same way as other, seemingly constructed representations where the emotional component seems added. In a thing presentation it is inherent.

Again, the best example is dreams, which are the experience of a somehow meaningful sensory presentation. Another dramatic example may be sexual experience. In all these examples, the meaning is experienced as qualities of the object because the affect is experienced as an inherent part of the sensory experience of the object.

In a thing presentation, percept experience condenses with affects and affect concepts. Affect and concept are experienced as percept. There has been a transmodal transformation of concept and affect into the percept system where it is represented according to the representability characteristics of the exteroceptive sensory system. The percept, affect and concept are condensed in the sensory experience.

This change in modality, from affect and affect-concept to precept, is very important in human sexual experience. The sensory system, so important in sexual stimulation and excitement, has the potential to experience and represent both the reality experience of the outside for which the exteroceptive system, including the proprioceptive system, is designed to be stimulated by, and also the experience of the inner emotional meaning reaction of intense affect.

Thing presentations are concrete representations of primary process and as such are not just content iconography but representations of processes. Qualities and quantities are processes and are often represented. Representation of processes is necessary in order to experience the qualities and quantities that are so infinitely variable and so richly compose the human experience, especially sexual experience. It is the process that is on a gradient and infinitely variable, as are the intensities and qualities of affects and of percept.

The thing presentation is a representation of the signifier and the signified, the day residue and the emotional associations, all together. The signifier and signified together is the symbolic representation that then refers to many related significant associated affects and their ideas.

Thing presentations provide a transmodal, sensory emotional, analog information system. This system is well suited for affect meaning processing. Qualities and quantities can be represented and manipulated in plastic representations providing a venue for infinite analog variations of quality and quantity and therefore of meanings and shades of meanings. Plasticity is also well suited for new syntheses with powerful veracity and validity experiences. These new representations can then be used for adaption to reality, to emotions, and to create an in-between state. Human sexual experience may use this sensory emotion system.

Human sexuality is a sensory experience and an affect experience and a concept experience and a physical experience, therefore we would expect it to be a perfect example of thing presentation processing. As in all thing presentation experience, in human sexuality the meaning is not only or even primarily about the experience. The meaning is in the experience. An example is a particularly favorite part of the sexual body of the other. It may be received as a reality thing with reality sensory qualities infused with emotional meaning experienced as qualities of the thing.

Example

A man may have a thing presentation experience of a woman's breast.

The physical qualities of the skin, its color and texture, the nipple, and its position, its arousal changes, may all be intensely exciting whether seen or imagined. It may be experienced as unique to the specific woman and a marker of that uniqueness. The experience may arouse other tender emotional feelings so that the man's experience is a feeling of being in love partly because of that breast and its physical qualities. He feels the emotional qualities when he sees or imagine the sensory experience and its qualities. He may say it is the perfect breast. He means it perfectly allows him to emotionally feel what he needs to feel with this particular woman.

Transitional Object Experience

Transitional object experience, a term coined and described by Winnicott, is the term for the experience of a dynamic interplay of the creative imagination in-between reality experience and emotional experience, which allows for the inter-digitation and transformational re-representation of reality experience and emotional experience. Transitional objects, the result of transitional ego processes, are fantasy mixtures of reality and emotional meaning. The key is not their condensation, which are characteristic of all symbolic representations, but rather the venue of experience of them. The experience of them is mental and it is the experience of neither reality experience nor emotional experience, but a mixture of both. That is the transitional object experience. Perhaps another name for this is imagination. Winnicott described the transitional object experiences as midway between reality experience and emotional experience, an object neither discovered nor made but both. The midway experience is a separate experience with its own qualities and its own characteristics. Inherent in the concept is the use of reality for symbolic purposes.

What is the difference between a symbolic alteration of reality, a thing presentation, and a transitional object? The symbolic alteration of reality is the large category with thing presentation and transitional objects subcategories. A thing presentation is an intense, fixed, sensory affect object suddenly experienced as properties of a reality external object. A transitional object is an in reality external object or a fantasy external object that is then experienced as a mixture of fantasy and reality.

An example of a symbolic alteration of reality is an artwork. An example of the thing presentation is a dream. An example of a transitional object is the toddler's blankie or an artist's canvas. Some feel the same about the sexual body of the other. Some feel this about the sexual body of the self. It can be about the relationship between the two sexual bodies.

The sexual body of the self or other can be experienced as a real object, an emotional object, a transitional object, or a thing presentation. The difference is where the object is located in mental experience and the qualities of the experience, and whether the meaning experience is a property of the self or the physical properties of the object. Transitional experience is a midway experience.

The experience could be any or a combination and is different at different times or in different self-states. The idea of a transitional object and transitional experience will be applied to human sexual experience.

Chapter 2

Symbolic Alterations of the Body

One type of symbolic alteration of reality, so important in human sexual experience, is symbolic alterations of the body. In symbolic alterations of the body, the object in reality and the emotional object in the self's mind, is the body. The body is being used to experience emotional meaning. It is a relationship one has with the body as surrogate for feelings about the self and the other.

The experience of the body of the self can be experienced both as an object and also as the self. This is why the body is a special symbolic representation; because the body of the self is both me and not me, both in reality experience and in emotional experience. It can therefore be a transitional object. The same is true of the sexual body of the other. It is both them and not them.

Because the body is a surrogate representative of the emotional self in the real self experience, it goes a step further than just emotional experience. Because emotions are experienced in the reality realm of the real body, symbolic alterations of the body have reality experience qualities. Anything that changes the actual physical body, like physiology function, or normal growth and development, or illness, or sexual arousal, changes the sensory experience of the real body. These physical changes have emotional meanings and are accompanied by emotional changes. To these emotional experience qualities are added reality qualities of experience. Thus do reality body changes make the real body fertile ground for intensely felt symbolic meanings. Because affect is felt in the real body and as a feature of the real body, it is only secondarily experienced in the emotional self.

Symbolic alterations of the body, a special type of symbolic alteration of reality experience, is the experience of strong emotions about and in the real body that change the experience of the real body. In symbolic alterations of the body, the mental is felt as physical. The physical has become a venue for emotional metaphor. Emotional experience is being experienced as a physical reality experience of the body. The "theater of the mind" is played out on the stage of the body.

DOI: 10.4324/9780429491733-3

Because the body is in reality experience, emotional reactions about the body and felt in the body may carry reality validity and veracity feelings. These can attach to the accompanying representations.

Anatomy and physiology are able to represent emotional experience because there is a physical experience. It is an emotionally meaningful experience, a real body as emotional metaphor composed of sensory emotions. This is especially true because of the changes in anatomy and physiology that occur during sex. Each change from what it was to what it is and back, and change itself can be a metaphor to represent an emotional state. The up and the down, the in and the out, the firm and the soft, the tender and the hard, the dry and the wet, the closed and the open, the giving and the taking, the bitter and the sweet, the strong and the vulnerable, the rigid and the yielding. These can all be harnessed for symbolic representation to express emotional change couplets: the awe and the contempt, the worship and the degradation, the idealization and the denigration, the superior and the inferior, the powerful and the weak, the strident and the meek, the beauty and the beast.

During the aroused state, it seems as though the symbolic meanings are real because they are linked to real changes in the body in reality, and the real body in the mind. The changes are caused by and cause an intense sensory sensation of somatic experience filled with intensely pleasurable lust affect. When felt in the body, it seems as though the emotional experience is real because the venue of the affect experience is bodily experience in reality.

Example

Ejaculation. What pornographers call the money shot. The ejaculating erection. The effective, desired conclusion. The QED. The power to do so. Thus, is the penis called the phallus. The word "phallus" refers to the emotional meaning of the penis, to its potency and power in intercourse and to inseminate. It also refers to an object relationship, power, and perhaps one of dominance. And there is always the exchange of liquid. From one to the other. From inside one to inside another. A special link. A deep emotional link. A magic potion and a religious experience of meaning in which the man has given of himself his manly meaning to the other who has taken him in. A boundary crossing connection of two lovers. A physical representation of a bonding glue for special attachment with a warm, spreading, internal emotional effect of intimacy. A union of mutual excitement and the endurance of excitement after separation. But for another, a symbol of contamination, of poison, of disgust, of fearful aggression and possession. Same phenomenon, different emotional content. Regardless of exact content, it is an experience of symbolic meaning of the body and the penis as a symbol.

Projective Identifications

"Projective indentifications" is a term Melanie Klein coined to refer to a certain type of projection. When affect and fantasy use the body as the venue for representation and symbolization, the body becomes the focus of projective identifications and projective introjections. These are emotional introjections from the self to the body and from the body to the self that occur in reality experience as well as emotional experience, because the body is real. But in symbolic representations of the body, what should be placed in one experience is placed in another experience, from reality experience to emotional experience and back then as a symbolic representation to the body. That is projection. In one form of projective identification, something is put from the self into the object, and is then taken back to the self, yet still experienced as inherent in the object.

The original source within the self is still denied.

Projective identification to the real body experience and to the real self-experience is the crucial aspect of these states. "Now I really am as I wish or fear I am." This statement represents a state change of the self-achieved through the reality body change. The experience of fantasy or of fantasy-reality mixes occurs in a changing reality body experience. Emotional meanings are now experienced as real.

In these states, there is a projection from the emotional self-representation to the real body experience where the real body experience undergoes symbolic alteration change and is then brought back to the real self-experience and then secondarily to the emotional self-representation. It then seems as though the origin of the experience is in the body, the real body, and not in the self. The emotional self-experience seems the result rather than the initiator. But it was the self from whom the original projection came. This is a description of sexual projective identification.

These projections and introjections occur on an ego function spectrum of neurotic to near-psychotic to psychotic. Projections to the body are vulnerable to this spectrum because the body is the real body and the introjection is to the real self-experience. Therefore, reality testing is challenged. What is emotional is experienced in reality and the ego function issue is whether the distinction can be preserved as a separate sentient experience.

Symbolic alterations of the body are seen in psychosomatic states expressing anxiety and depressive affect in their affect contents or ideas. Anxious depressive ideas of denigration and decay of the body are aggressive attacks on self-experience by hidden implacable emotional forces that are undermining and demonizing. The classic psychoanalytic descriptive term for this was "oral sadistic fantasies." More common are excretory fecal. But these fantasies have a variety and mixtures of emotional contents. Physical experience, real body experience, can also be pleasant and a venue for projective identifications and introjections of positive affect and positive affect ideas as in athletics or sex.

The change in the experience of the body due to a change in emotional experience of the body is what is meant by a symbolic alteration of the body. The real physical change and the emotional meaning of the change have become condensed and then the emotional change seems to be the real change. Everything following in this chapter and the next chapters can be seen as derived from understanding symbolic alterations of the body.

Sexual Symbolic Alterations of the Body

Sexual experience is a high affect state felt in the body. Sexual experience is a symbolic alteration of the body because as the body is undergoing changes during arousal, meaning is attached and evolves with the bodily changes. The result of sexual experience during arousal is not just of a state change of the body but a state change of the self. Sex and its changes are experienced as self-changes. The physical changes become emotional metaphors.

Sexual sensation in the sexual body of self and other are seen as special links to the beloved. Sex is seen as a unique connection, giving and yielding, secret and shared, all experienced through the sensory system as physical attributes of the self and of the beloved. This is an experience of sensory details that equate emotional bonding with physical bonding, first experienced in infancy where they were simultaneous.

These physical experiences were and are experienced via the sensory system. The qualities of the sensory emotional experiences are the qualities of those sensory system experiences. The body comes to self-experience through the sensory system. The interceptive system of bodily feelings and our observations of it, the exteroceptive sensory system.

The aroused body is a physically changed body. These physical changes have emotional meaning, causing the body to be experienced as a symbolically represented body as well as a physically changed body. The symbolic experience of the sexually aroused body is a proprioceptive and interoceptive sensory reality experience of meaning in the body self and other. Sexual arousal changes the body sensitivity threshold and opens it to heightened sensory reception, for example, of touch and the other's touch. This sensory experience is used as the day residue for the symbolic elaborations that will form the representations in sexual experience.

Sexual symbolic alterations involve not only the aroused body self but the aroused body of the other. Most intensely during sexual arousal, the body of the other is crucially involved in symbolic alterations and symbolic experience. The aroused other has intense emotional meaning for the aroused self. There are projective identifications and projective introjections to the body of the other as well as to the body of the self. The aroused real body of the other is an emotional metaphor just as is the aroused body of the self. The aroused body of the other changes feelings about the self. This is usually a crucial part of the sexual excitement experience.

Example in Men

A common example of an experience of the sexual symbolic alteration of the body is the experience of the erect penis. The penis is an anatomical structure. Psychoanalysts use the word "phallus" because they are referring to the common fantasy about the penis in which the penis has certain properties. The phallus is a fantasy about the anatomical structure. The fantasy is one of power. The erect penis has a certain experience feeling and look to it that easily allows it to symbolically represent feelings of influence, assertion, effectiveness, confidence, mastery and power.

Example in Women

This phallic genital fantasy also applies to women. An illustration of its application to women is when a group of 14-year-old girls suddenly entered a social gathering all decked out, short skirts, makeup, high heels, cell phones in hand. They made their entrance and marched in as a group, their high heels clicking against the floor. A senior woman analyst muttered under her breath: "Thunder pussy!"

This refers to their newfound power feeling of sexual attractiveness. Their bodies, now changed in adolescence to adult women with sexual anatomical markers, gave them new feelings of sexual power. It illustrates the body power fantasy as related to feelings and processes that come from, and to which may be recruited, different anatomical structures – the vagina and not just the penis. The term "phallic woman" refers to this, not to women with a penis but to women who can feel and assert personal and interpersonal power. They insert themselves into processes of change. They have an active effect on those around them.

Sexual Thing Presentations

Sex achieves its emotional goal and its power by altering the reality sensory experience of the body. Both the physical changes of the body and the emotional meaning of the physical changes, occur simultaneously. Because the intensity is often high in aroused states, the thing presentation experience can condense and emerge. Then the meaning of the physical change is experienced as the physical change itself, therefore, a property of the sexual part, rather than the emotional meaning of the sexual part. A thing presentation experience further validates the reality of the meaning. A thing presentation is a combination of concept, percept and affect. The affect concept is experienced in the percept of reality.

Human sexual experience is a high affect experience and therefore may have thing presentation experiences that are the sensory symbolic representations characteristic of all high affect representations. The shift to thing presentation condensations involve the trans-modal shift, trans-sensory, from emotion and idea to sensation and vice versa. Sensuousness is a synesthesia in which the visual and cutaneous properties of skin and of emotion become the sensory experience of an intense affect attachment to the object.

Thing presentation forms of sensuous sexual experience are a common modality of sexual experience. The sensuous properties of the sensory are experienced along with lust affect and its meanings as properties of the sensuous body in reality and not of the affect concepts in emotions.

Example

A 50-year-old man has had a lifelong enacted sexual fantasy. The peak experience of his arousal is the touching of the soft skin of the woman's inner thigh. He has a strong physical reaction to the softness of the skin and to the smoothness of his touch upon it. Then he feels the tenderness of the intimacy he has uncovered. He has reached the tender part of her. Then he can feel tender. He thinks of it, however, as a possession of hers rather than a meaning to him. It is her soft, tender skin and he is just responding to it. This is a defining characteristic of the experience of a thing presentation.

His associations are to the softness, the way it feels on his fingers. It seems to be a vulnerability, a yielding, a capacity to be gentle, and therefore to nurture. It seems precious and special. It seems an available offering for him, the revelation of which he is now invited to pursue. It is the access to the access, the sensuous waiting room, with a fantasy of inevitability, and of delayed access to the object of desire. It is a permission; the agreement and acceptance of him as a desired and worthy person. His fantasy is of the woman's allowing, or more accurately, acquiescing, to his touching of the inner thigh. The fantasy is that now he has access, the woman has given him access, to her genitalia and to her emotional life. She now recognizes, and is about to recognize even more, his influence and to be open to it and pleased by it.

He always pauses at that point, to savor the touch with a fantasy of being in the erotic waiting room, when the door is finally opening, to his touch, to receive him, for him to enter. When he was young, he would prematurely ejaculate at that point because when he gets to touch this inner thigh area, his arousal accelerates. With age, and the longer plateau phase, he can control it so it extends into coitus.

His wife is hesitant and anxious and he unconsciously experiences her as emotionally withholding but not out of anger or disapproval but out of anxiety. The anxious hesitant wife is the result of his object choice and not the origin of his experience. He has had this fantasy with all women but the eager ones disrupt his pausing at that point and thereby disrupt his pleasure.

In his work in business, he is a confident and patient number two and an anxious and insecure number one. Numbers three and four are intolerable and he strives hard to achieve and be promoted. He waits for the boss to offer the approval bonus at Christmastime. He has a special skill and feels it should be rewarded voluntarily and with thanks rather than used by him to bargain and to force. At work he is attacked by the Wall Street sharks and peripheralized and eventually has to leave because of their envy. They see what he can do and they can't. They undermine him and take credit from him. He relies on charm to seduce women, which doesn't work well with Wall Street sharks.

Skin eroticism often involves sensory qualities of soft, smooth, sensitive, tender. All of these qualities may be the sought after emotional qualities of the yearned for object. That which he imagines is hidden and withheld is now revealed and offered. These may be the missing qualities in the primary object relationship. No caressing, that is, no security of endearment. This sensory metaphor may also depend on a hypersensitive attunement to touch.

Lust Affect

Lust is the affect component of sexual arousal. Lust is a special affect because of its special experiential properties. Its most obvious property is its link to conscious bodily experience even at low levels of intensity. Lust causes a change in the body called sexual arousal and produces the sexually aroused body and the sexually aroused emotional mind.

Sexual symbolic alterations of the body are symbolic alterations of the body in which the major affect is lust. The sexual symbolic representation is organized by the affect of lust. Lust is not just the experience of physical arousal. It is also the experience of emotional arousal. Sexual arousal is both a physical state and an emotional state.

Lust affect has a particular quality that differentiates it from other emotions. Lust always changes the body in specifically sexual ways. Understanding sexual symbolic alterations of the body and sexual symbolic representations and fantasies requires understanding the special properties of lust affect.

The experience of lust has both a quality gradient as well as a quantity gradient. Both are consciously felt in the body at all increments of intensity. Each increment changes the meaning and makes meaning more complex. The intensity gradients and their mixtures add to the meaning of the emotional representation in the sensory system depending on the lust intensity in the self and in the sexual other.

Because lust causes arousal and arousal leads to body changes, and the experience of those body changes are symbolically altered by emotional reactions to the aroused body, and because this can coalesce into intense thing presentation experiences that are sensory emotional representations, sex isn't just about physiology and discharge. Sex is also about intensely pleasurable sensory emotional meaning. Its drive-like properties press for emotional satisfaction as well as physical satisfaction.

The more intense the affect the more it is experienced condensed, along with its symbolic representation of that affect, in the sensory system. Lust affect becomes intense sexual excitement and generates intense meanings. These intense affects recruit meaning along associational chains. It is what makes human sex experience so complexly meaningful.

Sex is meaning making. Sex makes its own metaphors. The emotional aspect of it and its meanings are often "hidden in plain sight" by the sexual form. The sexual form is so intense that it seems to be only sex. But the associational chains of emotional meaning go way past the sexual into the nonsexual. All are condensed and represented in sexual symbolic alterations of the body.

Lust condenses other affects into the disguised package of sex. The emotional lust meanings are greater than the sexual meaning. Intense surface affect of lust serves as a vent, to disguise and defend but also to release, the satisfactions of more complex emotional experiences that are hidden and represented in sex.

High affect states like lust strain ego boundaries and can leak across boundaries. Lust can be felt in, or be projected and introjected from and to, the self-representation and the real self and into and from the object representation and the real object. This is because the self in reality and the object in reality are similarly changing and are filled with similar lustful affect.

Those changes are coordinated during sexual arousal between self and other. Excitement in the one kindles excitement in the other. Lust can be a shared affect arousal and a shared state change. There is a bidirectional kindling of lust and body arousal in the self and between the self and the other, both emotionally and physically. Lust affect leads to intensely meaningful relationship exchanges for both partners.

Therefore central to the symbolic representations of human sexuality is the role of the sexual other; the sexual body and emotional response of the other. This becomes part of the reality day residue for the sexual symbolic representations of self and other. This means that because the body of the other and its changes, physically and emotionally, are a part of the lustful symbolic alteration of reality, and a trigger to the experience, and because excitement stimulates excitement in the body self and in the object body, there will be concordant and complementary identifications and introjections. It is important to realize that these projections and introjections are to and from real bodies and their changes. Two real bodies responding to each other are two bodies linked together as one lust relationship. This becomes represented in the physical body representations. Especially significant is the emotional experience of self and other sexual representations.

In sexual experience, projective identifications and projective introjections are to and from the body of the self and the body of the other, two sexually aroused bodies in both reality and emotional experience. The emotional meta meaning is:

> this really is happening in my body and their body, we really are changing, and thus I am now changed as I really wish to be, as I really wish I am, and they are really changed by me as I really wish them to be.

The emotional content is varied and complex. It is validated by the reality of the physical experience.

This change in the reality experience of the self and of the other can be intensely gratifying, or intensely frightening, intensely attractive, intensely repulsive, or a combination. Because these projections are not just to and from one's own body but also to and from the other person's body, the kindling of excitement involves these two bodies and their sexual changes in reality. That is the where the excitement and the meaning and the potentials and the anxiety and fear problems are because the situation depends not just on one's own reaction but on the other's reactions, as well as one's own wishes and fears.

Because sex involves the real body of the self and also of the other person, this meaning drama is done in reality. Even the fantasy is a fantasy of reality changes and reality experience. This reality quality gives sex a validity and veracity emotional experience of reality.

The Arousal Cycle

Lust occurs in a cyclical sequence. It is called the arousal cycle. The arousal cycle is a physical sequence of phase changes of the body and its mental representations leading to orgasm and post-orgasm. Sex is a sequence of physical and mental changes.

The arousal cycle involves quiescence/latency, readiness, arousal, excitement, plateau, acceleration/inevitability, orgasm, post-orgasm and then latency or quiescence again. Each of these phases is filled with important emotional meanings. Each phase builds in intensity until it triggers and catalyzes the next phase. A catalyst for the next phase is not just physical but mental; the meaning of the physical is what usually makes the physical a trigger.

Progress in the cycle may be quick or slow, and different at certain points, and with different sexual partners. The points of transition from one phase of the cycle to the next are crucial nodes of meaning. These are the thing presentation experiences and their symbolized fantasies that reveal the meaning of the node and why it triggers the next phase. The human arousal cycle may be shared; kindled in each by each.

Intense excitement of arousal may put the ego state of the person into an excited state. In that state, there is an increased sensitivity of the sensory systems so that sensations are more intense and their triggering quicker even at lower intensities. In addition, because arousal involves all of the emotional system, boundary function between all affects and all sensations are under strain and condensations can emerge of sensory emotional experience. If intense enough, they can take the form of a thing presentation. The aroused ego state, usually experienced as pleasant, may be experienced by certain neurotic patients as unpleasant. Many may find it to be both pleasant and anxious. The anxiety is because of the fantasies that are aroused. The fantasies have to do with the meaning of sex to the self and its associated sensory emotional contents.

The most sexually intense ego state of arousal is the orgasm, sometimes felt as in obliteration of meaning. But it is not an obliteration. It is a peak; a dense sensory emotional condensation with conclusory meaning whose significance is further worked through in the post-orgasmic lassitude. For those who experience orgasm as the culmination of meaning, entering then a state of pleasant, peaceful no meaning, this is the meaning for them and plays its important part in the meaning in their arousal cycle.

The stimulation of erogenous zones may result in a sexual response, the aim of which is to increase the level of arousal in order to enjoy the act and potentially reach an orgasm, but also to move through a fantasy, with enactment. Every erogenous zone is part of the sexual fantasy. The erogenous zones are different from person to person. The meaning of the same exogenous zone differs from person to person. The stimulation of the erogenous areas that some find pleasant and exciting may be difficult to bear by others. One person's excitement may be another's disgust. Sometimes it is both.

Sexual Fantasy

Because there is an arousal cycle with changes in the real body at each step in a sequence, and with each step a symbolic representation, each phase can be linked in a causal sequence of meaning; because of this then that. When symbolic representations are linked, we call it a fantasy or a story that can then reveal its plot, its motivations, its conflicts and its syntheses.

Sexual fantasy may be linked to the arousal cycle. The sequence of meanings produces fantasy with associated synthesizing themes and the themes impose themselves on the sequence. The meanings of the fantasy may be attached to the physical phases of the cycle producing a sexual meaning cycle.

The arousal cycle can be a story with a beginning, a middle and an end. And a beginning again. The story is composed of a series of physical experiences symbolically experienced. Those symbolic representations picture a change in the self-representation at each step of the cycle. It also pictures changes in the sexual other at each step of the cycle.

We can understand which steps in the fantasy are crucial because they trigger or conclude with the next phase of arousal. Orgasm is probably the most obvious of these steps. But all the arousal nodes are usually dense thing presentation condensations of meaning that describe the condensed changes in the self and object that make them ready for, and which usher in, the next phase.

The story is about changes in the self and changes in the other. They are linked changes of emotional meaning. Linked is a strong metaphor for attachment. This makes sexual activity a powerful attachment modality producing a strong type of bonding. The arousal cycle is not just about physical release. It is about the emotional meaning of attachment and its emotional satisfaction. When attachment causes anxiety and fear, it can effect sexual experience.

The orgasm is an intense symbolic alteration of the body with a dense condensation of meanings. Freud would call it a node of special meaning and the naval of the orange, the conclusory center of the story. There is also, a post-orgasm chapter to the story, which is the second ending. The first ending is the culmination ending of the intensity story; thus we see that. The second ending is the meaning of that culmination.

Fantasy is not only a road to arousal and orgasm; arousal and orgasm are a road to conscious fantasy. Physical arousal and orgasm are self in reality and object in reality phenomena that trigger real self and real object mental experiences. The reality qualities seem to validate fantasy. It is a physical, reality validation.

Sexual fantasy is collated. Each iconographic item and its meanings may be from a different phase of development and from a different primary object relationship. All have conflict themes of attachment, abandonment, traumatic aggression, special idealization, all sexualized into a sexual synthesis. The sexual fantasy or story often represents a mastery of these conflicted elements brought about by the plot of the story.

The arousal cycle can slow down or stop. It is called an inhibition. Therefore, the sexual arousal fantasy cycle can reveal inhibitions and their dynamics based on fears of attachment bonding and guilt or shame about its physical modalities of expression. These fears are the emotional content of the inhibition. Sexual fantasy uses the what and the how of sex to express and disguise the who and the why of human relationships.

The intense sexual lust experience disguises and represses major aspects of the fantasy story. It especially disguises the nonsexual motivations, fears, conflicts and compromises, and the history of traumas. Therefore, sexual experience must be analyzed to understand it. Sexual experience is manifest content. It is meaningful in and of itself but it is composed of derivatives of more unconscious fantasy. This means there is no one-to-one correlation between sexual action and phase of libido or phase of development. It is overdetermined and multi-determined.

The human sexual experience and its symbolic representations and resulting fantasy thus involve conflict and compromise characteristic of the person. It means that human sexuality isn't just about discharge of libido and the id but about satisfaction of personality dynamics. It is therefore especially vulnerable to neurosis.

A psychoanalyst works with human sexual experience by understanding and interpreting the emotional meaning of sexual experience. The more known about what is encoded and how it is encoded in the images and physical experiences, the actions and behaviors, and avoidances, of the arousal cycle and its fantasies, the more the analysis will progress.

Masturbation Fantasy

Stable sexual fantasy, if there is one, may be in a core masturbation fantasy or sex print that is characteristic of the person. It is a stereotype, singular or close cluster, of symbolic representation series whose details link to the arousal cycle and which tell a constantly repeating story, with different variations, that describes the different meanings and themes. The masturbation fantasy shows not only the wished-for sexual actions but also their linked wished-for emotional self-states and wished-for emotional object states. The fantasy thus reveals core personality themes. The masturbation fantasy is a core personality fantasy that is sexualized. Core personality dynamic fantasies are wished-for self and object relationship states.

Sexual fantasy therefore shows varying degrees of wish, fear, idealization, love, aggression, giving, taking, how to achieve these and their consequences. Therefore, it is a conflicted story. Sexual fantasy reveals the core neurotic elements and their defenses with unusual clarity. This is because the intense affect is bringing into consciousness the primary process representations of dynamic psychology with its motivations and fears, its defenses and adaptational secondary revisions.

Because sexuality grows and develops along with personality and object relations, human sexuality can tell you about the development of the fantasy, therefore of the person, ego development and the development of core dynamic conflict contents. Sexual fantasy can also tell about memories of reality. It makes sexual fantasy like screen memory in its structure.

The masturbation fantasy can change from incidence to incidence in its particulars according to different self-states; different states of self-esteem. These self-state changes will be reflected in the particular iteration of the core story. Masturbation, seemingly about sexual actions and sexual others, is also and primarily about the state and vicissitudes of the self.

Over time, the masturbation fantasy tends to slowly grow and develop if the person is growing and developing. It can change dramatically when there is a reality event that dramatically changes the person's self-esteem, for better or worse. The history of the masturbation fantasy is therefore a history of the growth and development of the person.

Example

An example is the inner thigh fantasy given earlier. It is an experience not only of the soft skin but the fantasy that accompanies it. Sexual fantasy may be with or without thing presentation experience.

In this case, the fantasy is linked to the arousal cycle. Looking at the appropriate anxious, withdrawn woman begins the arousal. The approach to the woman, the tender attitude, and her reluctant but vaguely positive response, begins the excitement. The embrace, kissing, consolidate the excitement. The approach to the legs, the opening of the legs and the touching and looking of the soft skin of the inner thigh, accelerates the arousal to the point of plateau and approaching inevitability. There is then the hurry to insert and thrust while maintaining the image of the voluntary opening of the legs for yielding, which brings orgasm.

The soft skin fantasy may be experienced with an actual other or in a masturbation fantasy or both. If it is a masturbation fantasy, it may not be enacted, but if it is enacted, it is always a masturbation fantasy. The exception is sometimes an action-oriented person, usually a woman, who enacts, claims it is being enacted at her rather than from her, and who claims that she does not have such a masturbation fantasy although she is clearly intensely excited to orgasm by the enactment. Often such a person denies any fantasy during masturbation. To a psychoanalyst, this is something of a distinction without a difference. Fantasy can be experienced in action only. This is true of the acting out of attitude in object relations for the nonsexual content emotional areas as well.

Sexual enactment is merely the expression of the fantasy in reality. Because masturbation is occurring with a real body of the self, just as the active fantasy is occurring with the real body of the other, they both use reality sensual experience as levers of enhancement of fantasy.

Human Sexual Experience as a Transitional Experience

Lust in self and body is attached to zones of body sexuality, with shared projective identifications and introjections, based on shared sensory experience, shared trigger zones, shared value zones, shared fantasy dynamics. Lust offers a potential for a mixture of fantasy and reality that is the essence of a transitional experience. It is that blurring of the boundaries between fantasy and reality, between emotion and body, between self and other, that offers a potentially creative space for growth and development. This is especially true for fantasy that seeks an interpersonal reparational conclusion. There may be enough of a plastic potential of different possible forms of the interpersonal repair.

Sexual arousal and fantasy occurs in both the self and the object, in the body of the self and in the body of the other person, in emotional experience of fantasy and in reality experience of the body of self and other. This simultaneous and sequential back and forth change of venue, interpersonal and intrapsychic, reality and fantasy, where excitement kindles excitement, of the self and of the other, of the body self and the emotional self, is crucial to sexual experience. They are special symbolic representations because the one is the stimulus for the other, and, thus, each may shape the representations of the other.

Transitional experience may mean shared between fantasy and reality experience of one person, two people, or aspects thereof, of emotional self and body self, or of sexual body self and sexual object body, or between the emotional self and sexual object body, or between the emotional self and the emotional object. Combinations are common. Arousal benefits from it. Romance requires it. Ambition seeks it. Anxiety inhibits it. Fear destroys it.

But there is a difference between shared and transitional experience. In shared experience, two people have a mutual experience, concordant or concomitant. In a transitional experience, two people are together orchestrating the experience between them. They are constructing a mutual fantasy with unconscious meanings for both of them and played out in reality. More importantly, this leads to and grows out of an experience of their mutual imagination. The transitional experience is one where there is an unspoken agreement not to question which aspects are real and which aspects are fantasy. The mental experience of both is that it is an in-between reality and fantasy experience. It is neither pure reality nor pure fantasy.

Shared transitional experiences elaborate and transform meanings for both and offer the creative space for each to contribute to building and transforming meanings for each other. The transitional product is both discovered and created because it both comes from within the self and is discovered in the object. It offers an opportunity for growth and development of object relations and growth and development of core personality. Transitional objects and processes are plastic, creative and changing, not fixed. They grow and develop. And so they can catalyze the growth and development of self and object. Sex can therefore be a venue for growth and development.

Shared transitional experience requires two people with the capacity to experience and use this type of transitional process. Sharing can be totally in reality enactments or solely in the fantasy. The ability to form and use transitional experience is an aspect of ego function. Sharing and cooperatively building is an ego function. It has its own developmental pathway.

Example

A lesbian woman finds her excitement accelerated when sitting as her lover kneels in front of her and extends her tongue partway when beginning cunnilingus. The tongue is described as little, meaning young; small, meaning tender and vulnerable; pink, meaning excited; and moist, meaning eager. Acceleration occurs when this exciting image is realized in reality. It indicates the excited acceptance of the willingness of the other to serve, to give pleasure, to the needs of the recipient, in an open and receptive way and to be excited by so doing. It is a fantasy of shared excitement that is crucial to the emotional meaning and satisfaction of the experience. Orgasm occurs with the actual lingual stimulation of the clitoris but more importantly in the fantasy, with the determination on the part of the supplicant partner to bring the dominatrix to orgasm, a goodly gift.

There is a post-orgasm experience for her that is also very important. It is the moisture on the lover's face. The fantasy about this is that it is a mixed combination of genital fluid and saliva. The mixture symbolizes the union of two people, excited by each other and joining together. This mixture is experienced as most satisfying, a visible symbol of their intimate, joyous union, eagerly sought and treasured by the lover. The idea of another person open to and excited by her and her desire, represented by her wet face, seems a deep acceptance of herself with all her wishes and yearnings.

Her partner is a creative lover and may extend the action with varying delaying tactics meant to increase the variation of excitement and therefore the sequencing of the story. The variation that increases arousal has to be actively felt by both and in that sense, is co-created in the transitional zone between and within them.

This example has illustrated the stepwise, progressive, linked experience of fantasy, enactment and the arousal cycle. It also illustrates the sharing.

Mutual Thing Presentation Experience

Both sexual partners may be having a thing presentation experience of their aroused body part or aroused body of the other. Sometimes the thing presentation experience is the same part, with an identical sensory thing experience in reality. It is then shared. The shared thing presentation body part then has the potential to be in the transitional space and to undergo creative recombinations that open a mutual pathway of growth and development. When these experiences occur, they cause intense and special feelings of bonding through enactment of, and development of, the story line. These feelings of bonding may be intensely pleasurable or intensely anxiety provoking, or both. They may cause intense comings together and intense comings apart, often repeatedly. They are one cause of the sexually addictive partner. Guilt or shame may trigger avoidance. But they can catalyze a deep, progressive and stable relationship. When this is truly a shared, exciting TP experience, there is the possibility of expanding this one-frame movie into a full-length feature.

Romance

Romance is defined as a special type of object relationship where the object is seen as special, unique, and is cherished with the highest valuation. It may also be sexualized and then the body of the other is idealized and cherished, not only the person.

Romance is a type of love. It has to do with the idealization of the other, of the relationship, of the body, of sexual experience, in a special type of union. Romantic love is a self-state and it involves all mental agencies. If one agency dominates, the dominant one depends on the strength of the agencies inherent in the personality. In some, however, the intensity and the conflict over attachment is an unpleasurable state and causes ego failures of synthesis or synthesis into frightening content.

Romance is a high affect state, a state of the self, a state of being. It is a motivated and motivational state of the self. A change into a romantic state is a change of the self. This is why it is experienced as potentially enlightening if all goes well and devastating if it does not.

It is a special type of attachment. It is called romantic attachment and romanticized attachment. Attachment is the crucial aspect of the romantic experience and of the romantic meaning of the experience.

Romance is defined as a particular affect content. First, there is a tender regard for a person seen as uniquely special and uniquely significant. The romantic object is an idealized object in reality. The mental experience is of a real object. Romance may or may not be expressed in sex and sexual feelings but if it is, romance is condensed with lust affect. Now the specialness of the tender object and the ideal object is the perfect sexual object as well. Second, often unstated, often unexperienced, but obvious to the observer, is that this uniqueness and specialness is their meaning to the person who has the romantic feelings. When the person in love says the other is perfect, what they should mean is, he or she is perfect for me.

Romance is a type of attachment. The goal is a belonging bond with a strong validating component. The strong validating feeling comes from the feeling that the romantic object is the ideal object and it makes of the self an ideal self because it is ideal to the romantic object. Romance is the transformational feeling. When the object is that special to the self, there is a yearning in the self to be that special to the object. The yearning is to be specially regarded, specially cherished, unique to another, needed by, and ideal to, the other and therefore uniquely and strongly attached, and therefore validated and bonded.

Romantic feelings produce a change in self-esteem because there is a change in the relationship to the self's ego ideal, producing a change in self-regard. There is a self-validation based on the object's validation of the self. Romantic affect content is about unique significance of the other and the self. This tends to idealization, hence to the projection of the ego ideal to the real object and the object in reality. This results in projective introjections from the real object and to real self. Romantic sex provides a pathway of introjection to the real self. The result is a feeling that two people are perfect for each other, infinitely unspoiled, inseparable, in an attachment that was meant to be.

It is important to realize that the romantic love involves an idealization that is felt as real. Special and unique mean ideal, and that reflects the ego ideal of the self. Romance, therefore is the projective identification of the ego ideal onto an external romantic object in reality. Hence, the object will have certain requirements for use imposed by the self and its ego ideal.

This inserts an element of danger into the equation. The dangers of romantic idealization are the conflicts between the ideal versus the real and the requirements for use of this ideal, which are based in the self, not necessarily in the object. The more the requirements, the more rigidly held, the more exaggerated, the more idealized, the more ambivalent-loved and feared, the more precarious will be the romantic attachment. The romantic relationship, to endure, must be a potentially plastic relationship because the object in reality never perfectly matches the ideal object and therefore the mixture must not be too fixed by the fantasy from the self.

The relationships that evolve under romantic stimulation are highly motivational relationships. Each has a potential for profound influence on the other. Romance may increase or decrease self-esteem depending on the personality structure of the self. The wish to please the romantic object in reality is also the wish to please the ego ideal and will be characteristic of the relationship of the self to its ego ideal; the relationship of core personality features of the self and its self-esteem issues. This is because romance and its experience depend on the relationship not only of the ego to the ego ideal but also to the superego and to ego experiences of the self-representation in love. These relationships are organized by the ego.

Neurotic romantic ideals involve the perfect object and the perfect body in reality. A more mature romantic ideal involves the more abstract perfect for me and perfect for us relationship. The neurotic romantic ideal is fixed in stereotyped content. The content has to do with static perfectionist objects. A more mature romantic ideal is flexible and complex and is process based. The neurotic ideal object is based on possession of the object with criteria of the self. A mature idealized object is based on qualities and criteria also of the object, with empathy for the object in reality. A mature personality is an integrated and stable one that can keep real self and objects from condensing with emotional self and objects in consciousness and upper layers of the preconscious, even as the emotional connection and fantasies are enjoyed at the conscious, preconscious and unconscious levels.

Neurotic Romantic Attachments and Core Personality Neurosis

In romance, the self-representation, the real object and the ideal object are condensed. The relationship of the self to the condensed romantic object will depend on the personality of the self (Fairbairn, 1952).

- The masochistic romantic ideal involves suffering for love, for the loved one, as a love offering to the ego ideal. There is a prioritization or an inflation of the object and de-prioritization or deflation of the self.
- In the narcissistic romantic ideal, there's a twinning experience with the object and the self as ideal. The self is ideal when linked to the ideal object. There is a potential inflation of the self and ideal object and a dangerous potential deflation of the real object to ward off a dangerous deflation of the real self.
- In the obsessive romantic ideal the goal is to control the relationship and the real object in order to control disappointment and loss in the self. It is an attempt to control a deflation of the self by controlling the object.
- The hysteric romantic ideal involves the enhancement of romance itself and the inflation of both the real object and the real self to prevent romantic disappointment and the deflation of the emotional representations of both.

Romantic Sexuality

Romantic affect may project to the body of the self and the other. This leads to idealized bodies and idealized sexuality. Romantic sexuality is on a continuum. The continuum is romantic idealization of part of the body, idealization of the entire body, idealization of the person in the body, idealization of the relationship with the person in the body, idealization of the capacity for growth and development with the person in the body. The capacity for this spectrum, and the placement of the experience along it, depend on different growth and maturity development phases of the ego. The romantic experience recruits personality development hence also personality traumas and conflicts.

Romantic love if shared offers an opportunity for shared growth and development: to understand, to be understood and to transform the relationship of the self to the ego ideal and to integrate better the self-representation, the real self and the ego ideal. The catalyst is the relationship to the real object which is the representation of the ego ideal. This has the potential to transform past emotional relational traumas. The shared opportunity for growth and development has the potential to traverse many phases of the life cycle. It most crucially can catalyze a better relationship of the self to the superego.

Love

There are four types of love, at least. There is romantic love, the in love feeling with a romantic object. There is sexual love in which one feels lust. There is companionate love or friendship love in which there is a nonromantic and nonsexual real object valuation of the mutually empathic relationship. And fourth there is commitment love, an infinite object and an infinite attachment. Ideally and maturely, love is a mixture. All love implies the concept of love of and for another. Mature love is about the other.

The challenge however, is to integrate these different types of love in the same person and the same relationship. Partial dissociations are common. There can be dissociation of romantic love from sexuality, there can be dissociation of companionate love from romantic love and from sexual love. There can be dissociation from commitment love.

Problems in love relationships are conflicts between elements that disrupt the synthesis. The problem with synthesis is the reason for the ubiquity of dissociations. The problem with bringing them all together is the worry that the one will spoil the other and not enhance the other. Whether or not bringing these different types of love together in the same person will spoil the love depends on the emotional experience contents of each. It depends also profoundly on past experience with love.

Once sex enters the romantic equation and needs to be integrated, the emotional experience of sex and its neurotic conflicts enters. This issue can be a spoiler. Because of the difficulty of integrating dissociations that are ambivalent opposites and intense, dissociations in this area may be secondarily assembled as mosaic objects in which the object is intact but dissociated internally. M. Kahn called them collated objects.

Therefore, romance and sexuality may or may not go together and may or may not be combined with commitment and friendship. Each has a developmental path. The integration of all four has a developmental path. Human sexual development of sexual function is the history not just of the libido but also of the ego, the superego, and their syntheses in the self. Human sexuality is a part of personality and reflects its growth and development. It can catalyze it.

Human sexuality develops not only continuously but as a series of stages. The stages are hormonally and socially driven. The stages are also driven by the stage of growth and development of the ego. The ego is involved in organizing the integration of human sexuality with the ego's objects and with interpersonal reality and for use as symbolic representations of emotional meaning. Sexuality can be used as a defense. When a new stages occurs, a reorganization of human sexual experience and meaning occurs.

Characteristic stages occur at birth, around two years of age, around four years of age, in late latency, in adolescence, in young adulthood, in middle age and in the elderly. Each phase of the development of libido finds an existing person with personality dynamics and ego organizations. Human sexuality condenses with personality attitudes about self and object representations. It does so in both reality experience and fantasy experience and in their relationship.

Sexuality helps synthesize the self-representation's growth and development with changes in the body. Sexuality is therefore part of the growth and development of our relationships to our bodies, to our object relations, to our significant others and to our attachments. Sexuality is an important part of the affect bonding glue of attachment. The history of sexuality is therefore the story of the experiences with significant others.

The growth and development of sexuality goes through a sequence of changes – in zonal states and focus, in capacity for object relations experiences, in dynamic contents of object relations stories, in dynamic content of zonal state and interactional sexual meanings, in arousal capacities and triggers, in orgastic capacity, in the ego organization of synthesis and depth and use, and in the ego's capacity for integrating sex and its meaning with the whole self and whole object experience and relationships. Lust hits before ego boundaries are solid, before abstract representations, with only concrete representations, before agencies are solidified, before synthesis of the sexual self, before conscious and unconscious barrier is strong and before affect modulation capacity is strong. Therefore, integration of sexuality is prone to conditions that increase intensity.

Sexual Fantasy

Sexual fantasy usually starts with adrenarche in late latency. Bodily parts and sexual zone experience, emotional themes of personality, physical or emotional trauma combine with the onset of lust capacity to produce fantasy and screen memories that represent this combination. Sexual fantasy therefore includes the history of object relations experiences. These experiences are with primary objects and with the primary self. This history of reality and fantasy is represented by physical reality of the body and its sexual arousal. Because of this condensation, sexual symbolic representation experience has the structure of screen memory. Screen memory is the picturing of one event at one level of development chosen to represent a mosaic of related emotional events and meanings. Memory is experienced in reality experience. The chosen reality experience serves both to represent and to defend against emotional experience.

Lust capacity hits an already established personality with an established core personality fantasy. There is an established attachment style. There is late latency age ego function of concrete representation and capacity for dissociation along with the early concrete symbolic representation capacity of that age. There is decrease foundering function capacity with increase stimulation intensity. This is true for both internal and external stimuli.

Lust capacity at any age hits an already established personality with a core personality fantasy about self in the world. There is an established attachment style. There is an appropriate ego function development including an age-appropriate symbolic function. When sexual fantasy first takes form in latency the symbolic function tends to the concrete representation. There is still a relatively immature modulation ego function for intense internal and external stimuli.

Latency is a developmental phase in the lifelong separation individuation process. Latency is a time when children separate a step further from their parents into groups and displaced primary objects. This phase of development and its attachment-separation issues find the ideal representation in sex whose physical mechanics can also represent attachment and separation. The emotional lust component seeking complement in the other is an ideal enactment for these attachment and separation issues. Love in this sense is the willingness and eagerness to be attached to a stranger.

Developmental Path of Love

In infancy, the intimate object and the sexual object are the same. At the Oedipal phase, the romantic object, the intimate object and the sexual object are the same; then romantic sexuality is dissociated and repressed. At adolescence, there is a reemergence of sex directed at the dependency object, which again has an abrupt dissociation that is repressed, emerging as a derivative in a reattachment to a non-incestuous romantic object but dissociated from other elements of love. In the young adult, there is a goal of reintegrating all four aspects of the love relationship possibilities with the non-incestuous object and autonomous dependency object. This rearranges the relationship between the self-representation, the superego and the ego ideal. In middle age, dependency growth of the commitment and friendship relationship is catalyzed by the crisis in the body ego ideal as middle age changes the body. This may combine with a mid-life crisis in the career ideal. It requires a new development of love and romance integration with the danger of a new dissociation. It is why the middle-age crisis is often called a second adolescence. It is because of the danger of a new dissociation of the sexual romantic ideal onto a new dissociated object. In old age, the crisis of the mortality of the body emerges and permanence requires moving the transitional object back into reality, and into memory past and into the future in search of the infinite object. The challenge is to remain engaged and generative and to see life as a continuous process, in a generational cycle, to which the self has and will continue to contribute to enduring transgenerational processes of value (Erikson, 1982).

The commitment and compassionate object links to the primary object of dependency while the romantic object links to the primary object of Oedipal sexuality and the primary object of the pre-Oedipal body. With trauma, the environment mother shifts to the object mother, from the traumatic or abandoning holding love of the mother to the more easily available and observable sexual body of the mother (Winnicott, 1971).

Because romance is a complex, high affect state of the self, conscious, preconscious and unconscious, from many stages of development, organized by the synthetic ego, the defenses against it often involve dissociations and not just repression and regressions and not just developmental delays, although the former may be a form of the latter.

The mature love object is a combination of the commitment object, the romantic sexual object, the dependency object and the aggression object. It is an integrated object. It is not a split object unless there is a partial dissociation along the ego spectrum with a split ambivalent object. Dissociation of the four types of love, of one or two types in this quatrad, will inhibit that one line of development and therefore will also inhibit the synthesis of all lines.

The fantasy potential of the romantic attachment is to change phase development trauma, which is reawakened. Examples are phase development conflicts about love, about attachment, about self-esteem, self-worth, causing long-standing stalemates in personality growth. The hope of romance is to change the self-representation. "Someday my prince will come" is a line well-known to all. The less well-known second line says, "and he'll change me." Therefore, part of the romantic fantasy is the nurturant union of acceptance, which will form a catalytic union to change or even to transform the self.

Chapter 3

Fetish

A fetish is defined as the sexual excitement and feeling of being in love with a part of the body or a thing in reality that is perceived as having special qualities (Marcus, E.R., 2020a).

An elaborated definition of the fetish would be that it is:

1. An object, inanimate or part of the body, that exists in reality, and is required in reality, for full sexual pleasure. It is required for progression through the arousal cycle to orgasm.
2. In the fetish experience, the fetish object is more important or crucial than the person.
3. There is romantic sexual idealization of the thing or part of the body, not the person, or of the person only because of the person's possession of the fetish object or body part. The patient is in love with the part.
4. The special quality of the object for producing excitement is seen as a quality of the object and not as a quality of the self but only as a reaction by the self to the exciting object. The fetish is therefore a sexual thing presentation.
5. The fetish is used to cover an inhibition, partial or complete, at one phase of the arousal cycle, usually defined as at arousal but most frequently at the transition from excitement to plateau or from plateau to inevitably of orgasm. The fetish is therefore an alternate path around an inhibition.

The fetish is a symbolic representation, a symbolic alteration of reality, in reality, that has a characteristic structure. This structure is an object in reality and its corresponding reality experience that is altered by emotional meaning to conform in reality experience to the emotional meaning. Reality experience is changed rather than changing feelings about reality. It is the same structure as the dream in which the day residue is symbolically altered. The structure involves an intense affect, lust and the projective identification of lust affect contents to the object and projective introjection from the object to the self. There is thus a projection of the fetish fantasy onto the real

DOI: 10.4324/9780429491733-4

object and the object in reality. This occurs across a disassociation boundary by experiencing the fantasy as separate from the self with the fantasy experienced as the property of the external object. The fetish experience of excitement crosses that boundary from the self to an externalized idealized, sexual thing presentation in reality and back again to the self. The fetish is therefore a sequence experience in which there is a change in the object in reality when it becomes sexualized, which causes a change in the real self-experience and therefore in the self-representation. The self gets the desired qualities through possession of the fetish object in sexual uses. The desired qualities are not conscious. The self does not realize there is a projection originating in the self because that process is unconscious. What is psychologically needed as a meaning experience is put into the object in reality by the self and then taken back by the self from the object but experienced as a reality quality of the object.

The step that is perhaps most interesting about the structure of the symbol is the need for and use of reality to represent lust experience. The motivation for the use of reality for emotional satisfaction in the fetish experience, as in all romantic experience, is the wish to feel that one really is how one wishes to really be. But in fetish, the experience is focused only on the fetish object.

Fetish of the body part is more common than fetish of a non-body object. For women it may frequently be the penis, but may be the butt, body stance, chest or arms. For men it may be the breasts, legs, butt, lips, hair or bodily stance. There is therefore a disguise in the fetish. It is a symbolic representation of a feeling state disguised as a body part or object, perhaps a normal body part.

The use of the fetish is a defense. It turns a feared love object and feared love relationship into a safe love object of secure possession, and a love object of longing and a feared relationship of loss into a love relationship of control.

The feared love object has caused an inhibition at an arousal node. The node chosen symbolically represents an aspect of the fear and the feared self and object state. The fetish is therefore a concrete representation of a permissive fantasy where the core masturbation fantasy is a required permissive fantasy and functions to allow normal arousal node function. It permits sexual function or pleasure. When there is an inhibition of orgasm, the fetish object allows acceleration out of the plateau phase into the phase of inevitability.

The arousal cycle is quiescence/latency, readiness, arousal, excitement, acceleration, plateau, inevitability, orgasm, post-orgasm, quiescence. Any one of those nodes may be affected by an inhibition and requirement for fetish use.

The fetish is a condensed compromise. It is a symbolic representation in reality of personality conflicts emotionally, disguised as a lustful symbolic alteration of the body or of a thing in reality, used as a reality lever to overcome a personality inhibition that extends outside of sex as well as in the arousal cycle.

The fetish often gets overlooked because it may be a normal body part. It may also get overlooked because the classic definition is content based rather than dynamic or use based. Modern ego psychology definitions are process based, ego function based and use based. They have variable dynamics and variable object contents. Originally in psychoanalysis the fetish was defined as content based. It was described as a fantasy a man with castration anxiety had about a woman with a fantasized penis accompanied by a disavowal of that reality. Under this content-based definition, a fetish was a symbolic female penis. Only men therefore had fetishes. This definition fails because phenomenology shows that a woman may also have a fetish. A woman may also have a fantasy about a female penis. But furthermore, the fetish can symbolize many different sexual erogenous zones and their meanings. It can also include both Oedipal and pre-Oedipal dangers, not just castration anxiety. Often the fetish is a multiple meaning, multi-zonal condensation of fears and wishes and defenses. It is a compromise formation in reality to which there is an intense, erotic, romantic, idealizing, powerful object relationship transference. The fears are not sexual fears but rather intimacy, attachment, ambition and possession fears symbolically represented by sex; the zones and the acts.

Fetish Thing Presentations

The fetish instrument or fetish part of the body is almost always a thing presentation. It has intense sensory emotional qualities of highly condensed emotional meanings that are seen as properties of the thing in reality rather than how the person feels about that thing. The physical qualities of the fetish carry the lustful emotional charge. They may be visual, tactile, olfactory, gustatory, or all. Qualities can be described in detail because they are so emotionally meaningful. It seems as though the full emotional meaning is reduced and captured by those details.

At the core of each thing presentation node of sensory emotional excitement is a core affect idea, with many iterations and associations. One core idea is acceptance. Another core idea is yielding. It refers to an attitude change in the sexual other that the fetish object has the power to produce.

A thing presentation is the sensory experience of the change or the certainty of change; some wished for, needed, exciting, represented, symbol of change, in the object appearance or behavior, that represents the change in object attitude. In a fetish, the fetish instrument is what has the power to produce that change. In the fetish enactment, it is the enactment that produces the change.

Example

A 40-year-old man has a spanking fantasy. The experience is enacted with women who like this, but his main excitement focus is on the paddle that he uses. He describes its qualities very specifically. It is wood, solid, firm, very smooth, dark, beautifully polished. Each quality is important. It is the size of a ping pong paddle. Just looking at it is arousing. Feeling it, handling it, is even more arousing. Looking and touching are the exciting sensory modalities.

His associations are to the sensory qualities. Firm and solid yet smooth and beautiful are key. Like the women he is attracted to. Beautiful, reserved, solidly organized psychologically, firmly boundaried, aloof, her sexual passion kept dissociated from him and partly from her. But how to make such a woman yield to passion, his and hers? His associations are to the paddle, its aesthetic beauty, and to its performance functionality, the solid feel. The look is the pristine and the functionality is the power; her pristine, him with phallic power. But because of his phallic insecurities and inhibitions, the phallic power is in the paddle. The ideal paddle stings but doesn't hurt. He feels this as a property of the paddle, not the controlled force of his hand. The ability to sting is the ability to call the woman's attention – to the paddle and therefore to him. It is to make her yield to her passion for his power. This is his fantasy and some of the meanings in his paddle fetish experience. The fantasy is a condensation of the fantasy phallic woman and his wished for phallic fantasy of his penis and his sexual appeal and prowess.

If masturbating, he holds the paddle and may touch his penis with it as he builds the excitement and plateau phase toward orgasm. Similarly, some women hold their vibrator while they masturbate, even when they don't use it to directly stimulate their genitalia.

This paddle fantasy occurs in women as well as men. Interestingly, the components and meanings may be the same. One should expect this because it is enacted bilaterally. How each find each other and how each come to understand to enact the fantasy is a story in itself and often an anxious, exciting part of the fetish enactment, although often overlooked, as is the resultant relationship after.

Fetish and Ego Function

It is the ego that organizes representations and fantasies from wishes and fears and the sensory impressions and thing presentations, charged with affect, that can be assembled into representations. Therefore, alterations and disturbances in the sexual function often correlate with disturbances in the symbolic function and reflect ego problem issues.

Fetish phenomena are on ego functions dimensions. There are partial fetishes or fetishized experiences that are not required for sexual function.

Freud said these are common, even ubiquitous. The diagnostic continuum of fetish and fetish like phenomena therefore proceeds according to need requirements and according to requirements of reality to fulfill that need. Because we are talking about the relationship to and requirements of reality, we are talking about ego function. In this sense, there are various corresponding ego function spectra.

There is the spectrum of need and what the need is for. The nature of the need defines the nature of the use and there is a use spectrum. There is the spectrum of intensity. There is the spectrum of dissociation. And there is the spectrum of reality testing. It is these spectra which together make up the spectrum of normal to pathological. The category normal-abnormal should be dictated by phenomenology of ego function.

The ego function requirement encompasses where the requirement is required. Is there a requirement of reality experience? Of the object in reality or only the real object in the mind of the self? Of reality testing? How firm is reality testing? Is there a requirement for a whole object as well as a part object fetish? The requirement axis has stations along it of arousal, orgasm, pleasure, maximum pleasure or satisfaction. The requirement component moves from required for biological functioning to required for psychological satisfaction.

Reality testing access moves from reality testing always negative, the psychotic state, to reality testing negative only in the aroused state, the near psychotic, to the neurotic with reality testing always positive even in the aroused state. The stability of reality testing in the face of affect intensity is one measure of ego strength. When reality testing is gone, the problem isn't the sexual content of the fetish, the problem is that reality testing is gone. This is an ego function problem not a sexual content problem. It should also be noted that there are varying degrees of concrete experience, varying degrees of thing presentation rigidity, and varying degrees of validity in reality. These are all subcategories of the reality experience spectrum.

The dissociation axis goes from narrow, in the aroused state only, dissociating only part of the self and part of the object, to wide dissociations involving the entire object or the entire self. Such wide dissociations separate with anxiety the self-experience from the object relationship experience and from other aspects of the sexual and nonsexual self-experience, either only during the aroused state or chronically, to some extent, even in the unaroused state. Such states are called depersonalization if they are dissociations of self or derealization if they are dissociations in the self of the real object. The crucial questions are two. Is the process occurring in sexual behavior only? How wide are the dissociations when not in the aroused state?

Observing ego is a separate ego capacity of self-observation and experienced as an aspect of self-sentience. It may, however, be dissociated from self-experience, or dissociated from action and the object. The axis is along the arousal axis of intensity. Milder forms dissociate meaning of the event rather than the event itself.

Another axis involves the area of ego experience. This axis is the relationship of emotional experience to reality experience to transitional experience. Back-and-forth oscillations and partial combinations are common. But when emotional experience is taken as reality experience and when there is no transitional area of imagination, then the ego function of organizing and relating of ego experience is damaged.

A way of summarizing this is to ask what are the ego functions allowing the aroused fetish experience to remain in fantasy and not capture reality experience in some way. This is the measure of ego dysfunction. If the fetish remains only in fantasy, even as a permissive fantasy, by definition it is not called a fetish. It is called an enabling fantasy. This is arbitrary. But the definitional term fetish makes note of the capture or partial capture of reality experience, and the necessity of this capture for sexual function.

These axes again bring up the issue of normal or abnormal, the definitions of which are fraught. Normal isn't necessarily common and common isn't necessarily normal. The fact is that anatomical preferences are ubiquitous as arousal levers and part of the sexual signature of everyone. They provide sex with special representations that have special pleasures and meanings. Ego dysfunctions allow not just the coloring of reality with meaning but rather the capture of reality with organizing emotional content. Abnormal involves the requirement spectrum and the reality testing spectrum. A fetish is required. A preference is not required. A variation is for variety only. Special meaning is not required for function, only for maximal satisfaction.

Fetish and Defenses

Defenses in human sexual experience involve repression of painful emotional associations that sexual symbolic representations disguise. The fetish defense involves romantic sexualized idealization. Sexualization is a defense against sexual and attachment bonding that may trigger fears, including fears of retaliation by rivals and abandonment or domination by the object. But because the fetish sexual representation itself triggers anxiety, shame, guilt and fear, dissociation often is also a part of defense maneuver.

In dissociation, one conflict is kept separate from another conflict. Splitting is a type of dissociation in which all good and or bad objects are kept separate. Often in sexualization and its dissociations, each side of the separate dissociation is mixed, both good and bad. Dissociation is usually inherent in the functioning of fetish and its idealizations. Dissociation and its mediating anxiety is the proof that the fetish is a symptom and not just a sexual variation.

Crucial to the fetish experience itself is the dissociation of the fetish from the object person. Love, romance, idealization and dependency are disassociated from attitudes and attached to the fetish object, which is experienced as separate from the rest of the object person and from the self. The part object of excitement, the fetish, is separate from the person. The person whose body part is the fetish, or to whom the external fetish will be applied, may be liked, loved, hated, or uninvested but is seen as separate from the fetish. How wide the dissociation is one of the measures of severity. The dissociation is not only of the fetish from the person but also the feelings about the person versus the feelings about the fetish.

The expression "he or she's hot," as observed by the self, is a property of the object and in the fetish experience is a dissociation from the more accurate statement "I'm hot for him or her." In the fetish experience, the self experiences the fetish object as primarily exciting rather than the self being primarily excited by it. Excitement is dissociated and becomes the property of the thing or part object.

An example is the man after a date with an idealized woman whose beauty was a fetish for the man. When asked by his buddy if he liked her, the man replied, "her body, her mind, or her personality?" His buddy said, "all three?" The man responded, "wow, eh, ugh!" The man was romantically infatuated with her body. He dissociated the parts that he didn't like from the part that he did like. Lost was the synthesis that we call the person. This is because the only part of the person he really liked was the body.

Sexualization and its dissociations protect the self from the whole object experience of the other and its bonding dangers such as abandonment, humiliation, domination, retaliation, parasitizing or disinterest felt as spurning, and therefore of aggression. But sexual excitement as a defense against emotional attachment to the whole object may lead to the danger of intense attachment to the fetish and the original fears reappear even though the locus of excitement is the fetish and not the person. The fetish is experienced as more easily possessed and therefore controllable than the whole object person but still dangerous, especially if it is addicting and captures the self.

When the fetish is a defense against a feared and ambivalent dependency but because of sexualization becomes an addiction, the self enters a frantic circular behavior in which the exciting but feared object is sought and discarded over and over. For those addicted, they may also come to hate the fetish as well as be excited by it. They experience themselves as helpless before it, which is the return of the original fear about being in love with the person. Once the excitement is in the fetish then it holds the key to sexual excitement and pleasure but it also holds the original, feared dependency. This is one reason for destroying the external fetish or the fetish object relationship, repeatedly. It is to be free of the enslaving object without realizing the slavery comes from the self's attachment need and fear. When it is an addiction, the major problem with sexualization is that it tends not to be able to ever satisfy the needs of the self.

Less obvious are the dissociations within the fetish itself. Fetishes, as Massoud Kahn points out, are collated objects. Collated means a mosaic, a collection. The collection is of specifics, with each detail a treasured possession, status nascendi, unintegrated. The fetish contains an emotional story that cannot proceed to synthesize or develop. The progression of the story is through the arousal cycle sequence, each step dissociated from the others, rather than a true integrated developmental story. But the sequence reaching some sexual conclusion with each arousal cycle, even if unintegrated, may offer the only path for satisfaction because the elements are conscious only during the lust cycle. But they are a sequence of mixed unintegrated story elements. The story elements are multiple manifest contents with multiple meanings. These different elements have good and bad features from which the fetish experience tries to isolate the self. When this fails in reality, the experience is spoiled and sexual excitement disappears. But the satisfaction sought for integration that fails is a strong part of the addiction repetition compulsion.

The dissociations disassociate physical from emotional, body from relationship, fetish objects from whole object, experiencing fetish self from experiencing whole person self, sex and romance from the real relationship, sex from love, idealized part from debased whole, ideal self from debased self, attraction from fear, love from hate, object mother from environment mother, and acute trauma from strain trauma.

Sexualization is an effective defense because the lust excitement focuses the attention only on the sexual, leaving the other elements hidden in plain sight. It allows discharge of attachment conflicts in personality dynamics without experiencing them as part of the self. The what is conscious although dissociated. The who is represented. The why is repressed. The wishes and fears are not only sexual but core personality wishes and fears. Sex is an attempt at a compromise that has more of the wish and less of the fear. When the intensity is such that a thing presentation experience is formed, the meaning of the stereotyped symbolism of concrete, intense, in reality elaborated meaning is rigidly dissociated and repressed.

Fetish as Transitional Object

A transitional object is an object in reality that is used by the mind to elaborate an imagination experience leading to growth and development of a mental capacity. In that state, the experience of the object in reality changes – develops. It is used as part of the fantasy. There is a story there that unfolds over time. The object and its meaning are in a kind of dialogue with in the self. There is a kind of sharing between reality and fantasy.

The transitional space is in the self between the real self and the real object, but can also be real object and the object representation and between the real self and the self-representation. When the sexual object is widely dissociated and exaggerated between the real properties and the emotional properties, and when the sexual self and the real self are likewise widely dissociated, then the fetish may be able to serve a useful purpose between the two. The fetish object can be neither one nor the other and yet have properties of both in a first attempt at integration of the two sides. Because the fetish is controllable and contains the sexual excitement safely within it, it represents the first step at integration and may reduce the danger enough for a second step, the relationship to the fetish, and a continuation of growth. This may especially be true if both sexual partners participate.

Sometimes the fetish experience can be shared with the person who owns the fetish object or to whom it is applied. Sex with the fetish object becomes a shared meaning experience. If romanticized, it can be an intensely shared romantic sexual experience. The fetish becomes a shared meaning experience. Shared fetish experience with another person allows for a sharing relationship. The possibility of sharing may open the possibility of growth and development within the fetish experience and therefore the possibility of growth and development of the self, as well as in the relationships between two people. One opens the possibility of the other. When meaning is shared, the possibility may open to both contributing to progressively elaborated, deeper meanings. The possibility of sharing the progressive enacted and re-enacted story of meaning, may open the possibility of growth and development of the self, of the object and of the relationship.

Both the self and object have to have ego structures that are flexible enough to allow for this possibility. It is a mutually written script of object relations. It begins with the object indicating in behavior,

> I will really do this and feel this with you and for you because I really am turned on by it and therefore by you so I can become who you really want me to be so you can become who you really want to be, and together, in this way, we can discover who we want to be and therefore who each of us can be.

Dissociation of the fetish from the self to within the couple allows expression of personality dynamic conflicts without the locus of conflict being in the self or between the couple. This is a way of handling personality anxieties about the self and the object and the relationship of attachment. The dissociation makes it easier to handle the anxiety because the anxious aspect of the self becomes a property of the fetish and the two people when in arousal and experienced as a not me not you when not aroused.

Evolving sexual fantasy permits evolving personality fantasy and therefore growth and development of the self. This is true for any intense, deeply shared emotional experience over time. A nonsexual example is raising children together when that experience is a conjoint, creative venture.

Transitional experience is the sharing between reality experience and emotional experience, then and now. This defines the imaginative transitional experience. The result is a shared intimacy of great emotional meaning and power. Examples of this in literature are *Who's Afraid of Virginia Woolf* and

Fifty Shades of Grey. In both, the story and the characters evolve and the relationship is slowly seen as vastly more important than the sex.

But the attempt to share may trigger a superego attack of shame and guilt causing anxiety and a wider dissociation. Or the attempt to share may trigger a fear of addiction to and control by the object, causing an attack on the object and termination of the relationship. This can be devastating because it represents a return of the original dissociated fear and loss.

There is a developmental sequence in the ego's capacity to form whole integrated objects as opposed to collated objects. There's a developmental sequence in the ego's ability to form and use symbolic representation. The sequence goes from concrete to abstract.

Development is the story of the ego's changes in its handling of representability, use of the resultant representations, of the capacity to experience yet boundary excitement, both sexual and aggressive, to be able to use transitional processes, to assemble and use whole objects, and whole selves. Development results in an integrated fantasy of the self that is not fully conscious. This unconscious fantasy has conscious self-narrative derivatives, which allows for progressive changes of growth and development of the self and the experience of the other.

Trauma interferes with this developmental sequence. The trauma may be physical or emotional, overstimulation or abandonment, or both. Abandonment trauma may involve not the loss of the object but the unreliability of the object emotionally. It may involve physical or emotional abuse which yields hated and feared internal objects. Another form of aggressive object is when the love attachment is used to emotionally parasitize the subject. These losses and deprivations may lead to a dissociation between the unreliable environment mother of loving processes and the object mother of loved stable body with love focused on the more reliable body object.

Fear of rage causing abandonment, so-called pre-Oedipal dynamics, and increased fear of Oedipal competition anxiety, manifesting as castration anxiety, itself a representation of physical or emotional attack, may be infused with abandonment anxiety. These are some of the motivations causing the dissociation between the person and the part object.

The trauma dynamics of a primary relationship are symbolically represented in the fetish object; its use and unconscious story. An example may be some types of voyeurs who are never the apple in the eye of their mother or only contingently.

In trauma's relationship to the fetish and representability, it isn't only the acute traumatic event nor only the frequency of the traumatic event, but also the chronic strain trauma of processes for which the acute trauma event introduces conscious representability. Acute trauma may be minor but has power because of its usefulness in representing the chronic trauma. This is particularly true when the chronic trauma is a subtle emotional deprivation, an absence, in the relationship and the acute trauma is an obvious event.

Lust hits before adolescence, during the adrenarche of late latency. It hits before full adolescent physical changes. It hits before adolescent intellectual development during which there is a burst of cognitive ability into the abstract. Lust hits an immature ego of immature cognition and immature personality. It hits in an interpersonal and social context. All of these contribute to sexual fantasy and to the concrete symbolic representation of the fetish, which may begin in later latency but flourishes in adolescence.

Development is layered. Because of multi-developmental layers, there is no one-to-one translation of manifest content. A fetish could represent a penis, a breast, the fecal stick; the process could be oral, urethral, anal, incorporative, excretory, genital, or all. It's not the object, it's the fantasy about the object. Fantasies are conscious, preconscious and unconscious.

Development of the sexual object corresponds with the ego's development capacity of object relations, whole objects, and of the four developmental lines of love. When there are fetish phenomenon, expect developmental histories of ego development problems. Trauma can interfere with ego development. So can learning disabilities that involve executive dysfunction. This can shift cognition in the direction of concrete representations, trouble with different levels of abstraction and trouble with maintenance of affect validity at higher levels of abstraction, trouble with integrations and syntheses, and trouble maintaining a transitional process and experience. Mood disorders may do the same thing to ego dysfunction because of increased affect intensity and its challenges to synthesis and flexibility of cognition.

Intense affect crosses boundaries and intensifies self and object relations making integration of good and bad aspects more difficult. Ego problems of boundary function that don't function to modulate intensity make sexual arousal dangerous due to its intensity and difficulty containing it. The link to attachment may be unpleasantly strong and conflicted, therefore, avoided. Increased stimulation causes increased emotional reaction, causes increased difficulty with integration and synthesis, because affect disrupts self and object continuity and triggers projective identification and introjections with their primary process intrusions. The intensity also changes processes and abstract content with their affects into concrete representations and thing presentations. This may cause an intense transference of past traumatic relationships to the present.

In these ways, romantic and sexual attachments may be in themselves traumatic. Then the problem is how to become sexually aroused without triggering the fear. Displacement of excitement onto a fetish object is one solution to the problem. But in mood disorders of some types, sexual desire and arousal may be very intense therefore making the fetish or sexualized solution a problem in itself because it, too, is so intense.

Chapter 4

Fetish Enactments

A fetish enactment is any stereotyped behavior necessary for progression through the arousal cycle. The behavior is usually compulsive, necessary, relatively irresistible, stereotyped, filled with sexual excitement and perhaps romantically infused. Behavior must be performed in reality and not just in fantasy. This is a use definition not a content definition. It doesn't matter what the psychological content is. The definition hinges on whether its use is required, in reality, for sexual function. The definition of sexual function varies from physical function to pleasure.

Sometimes the action is covert; disguised in different ways. One way is for a tiny piece of it to be enacted that symbolizes the entirety. Another way is as a highly disguised derivative so that the true content of motivation is hidden. Sometimes it is betrayed only by the stereotypy of the prescribed sequence of sexual behavior, the manifest content being unremarkable: it is disguised as a habit pattern rather than a requirement. Its true meaning remains in fantasy.

The behavior may be a single enactment or a series of linked enactments but they are part of a sequence that tells a story. Some aspects of the enactment story are conscious, some preconscious and some unconscious. Behavior is called an enactment when the behavior is expressing a story, an emotional story of meaning, also called a fantasy. Enactment is the enactment of a fantasy.

The fetish action is more important for sexual function and pleasure than the person at whom the action is directed or of whom the action is required. Their role function is more important than their person. What they do is more important than who they are. Their importance is their willingness to do or to perform the action even if not excited, but preferably to be excited, by the actions, or at least to feign excitement. But their interest and attention to it is usually good enough. Depending on the content of the action, the response of the object may be in addition or instead of excited: interested and curious, anxious and afraid, frozen with excitement, cold but interested. An intense response of some type is usually required. This signals that the perpetrator is having a strong, real emotional effect on the real sexual object.

DOI: 10.4324/9780429491733-5

What type of reaction required is an emotional reaction and varies with the content of the fetish enactment fantasy.

A fetish is a static object. A fetish action or enactment is a static performance. Fetish enactment is a required, stereotyped, sexual drama with required participants, required actions, required responses, required sequences and a required ending and post-ending in a stereotyped script, either actively performed or provoked. It may be both a static fetish object and an action.

Example

Miss P, with rigid control of her own romantic sexual excitement, becomes excited with her active seduction and control of the sexual object. She orgasms with digital entry into the man. The tightness around her finger as she penetrates is the sensory thing presentation of psychological resistance but irresistible yielding, to her strong phallic power, her fetish finger insertion overcoming the resistant but secretly vulnerable object. Now she is the one in control. She seduces the man into it, she says. This seduction is exciting to her and starts the arousal cycle.

The object's attitude to the action and change in attitude during the action is the crucial part of the action purpose. The change in attitude of the object is ostensibly a change in behavior but is actually a change in attitude to the perpetrator. The action helps disguise the purpose of the action, which is not primarily to elicit a response of action but, rather, a change in attitude because of the action. This change is signaled and symbolized by a response to the action. The real important change is the change on the face of the object during the action, which reveals the change in attitude. This is often not conscious.

Outside the sexual drama, the relationship to the loved object varies from free of fetish enactment dynamics to infiltrated to dominated. The healthier the person, the more mature their ego function, the less sexual desires and dynamics dominate the entire relationship. In the mature, if there is any sexual dynamics contamination of non-aroused object relations, it is as a highly disguised derivative or a reaction formation against it.

The required sexual enactment is usually an enactment of the core masturbation fantasy used as an alternate pathway to orgasm and sexual excitement. The inhibition is most commonly at one arousal node of the arousal cycle. It is most commonly at the orgasm node with a resultant delay or arrest in the plateau phase, or at the beginning of arousal or both. The fetish enactment is to help overcome the trauma history of abuse or abandonment that has triggered fears of attachment, humiliation, castration, or betrayal, fears that interfere with steady progress in the arousal cycle because anxiety is triggered.

The purpose of the fetish enactment is to overcome the inhibition by a hoped-for transformation in reality. The reality transformation required is the transformation of the real self-experience through a transformation of the experience of the object in reality. Inherent in romantic idealization is the wish for transformation of the self. Inherent in fetish action is the transformation of the object, from a feared to a controlled love object.

Fetish enactments occur along many continua of ego functions. They are the same continuing as described in Chapter 3 for fetish phenomena. The spectrums are the requirement-pleasure spectrum, the reality testing spectrum, the transitional object spectrum, the relationship derivative spectrum, the whole object spectrum, the dissociation spectrum and the observing ego spectrum. All are describing specific ego functions relevant to the organization of object relations and the use of human sexuality. All are describing different aspects of the experience.

Fetish enactments occur in both men and women. Both men and women may require the permissive role of the action. When a man and a woman engage in such an enactment, one may assume that both find it meaningful. Sometimes it is perfectly concordant. Even if it is merely a yielding, that is a type of participation and therefore meaningful. It may be a crucial, aspect of the story.

Inhibition

One of the functions of the fetish enactment is as an alternate pathway around an inhibition. These inhibitions are psychological structures whose content differs from person to person and from personality to personality. The classically described case is in the hysterical personality.

Swept Away, as in the movie by the same name, is the metaphorical experience of passion. Waves of passion. This is a description of the excitement phase of the arousal cycle. Passion is a sensory affect contents.

Hysterical sexual inhibitions may manifest as being stuck in the excitement phase of the arousal cycle, even outside the sexual situation, but they suddenly lose their excitement and resultant lubrication during the mid to late excitement phase of the arousal cycle and don't progress to orgasm. This is called Female Genital Arousal Disorder. They avoid sex or the sexual object of passion or they dissociate it into a separate, hidden relationship or they counter-phobicly enact it over and over. They may have other inhibitions and avoidances in the arousal phase or other phases of the cycle such as orgasm. Hysteric female patients may sexualize the relationship to avoid sexual performance, which they phobicly avoid. As the old saying goes, everything then becomes about sex except sex. Countertransference in the male analyst may be feelings of attraction but annoyance and fear of rejection if confronting.

Hysterical men may show ejaculatio praecox and ejaculate while losing their erection during the early excitement phase or suffer from performance anxiety and lose the erection at time of penetration. In both male and female, these performance issues may be based on phallic insufficiency anxieties, which mean low self-confidence in situations of assertion even though some seem very confident, that is to say, overconfident. They may have great enthusiasm but poor follow through in many of their life challenges.

Obsessive inhibitions usually manifest in a more subdued excitement phase and in the male, ejaculatio retardata, and similarly in the female, delay of orgasm. Obsessive patients have trouble relinquishing control, even to their own bodies and their own sexual excitement.

Those with fetish and particularly fetish enactments use this modality as an alternate pathway around the inhibition. The reason it works is that it allows the enactment of a different set of sexual contents, a less anxious one. It allows a diversion of sexual excitement to a different object and or aim; for instance, oral-genital instead of vaginal intercourse. This allows progression through the arousal cycle to its culmination and satisfaction.

Fetish Enactments and Symbolic Representation

The sexual enactments are a special type of symbolic alteration of reality. They are lustful attempts to use sexual actions to change the reality experience of the other person and therefore of the self. Enactments direct reality to conform to a required fantasy. In changing the experience of the object in reality, the subject hopes to change the reality experience of themselves. The wish to change the object in reality is in order to change the emotional self-experience via the experience of the real self. This is in order to counter a problem in self-esteem. It is the use of reality to help with something that is emotional. It is the use of the other in order to help with a problem in the self. Such people really do and have done to themselves in order to really feel different about who they feel they really are. They really want to do and to really be done to in order to change their experience of themselves in reality. If it is made real perhaps their feelings about themselves can change. If it is true in reality then maybe it can be true emotionally.

The specific structure of such symbolic alterations of reality is to use a change in reality as a day residue core of a symbolic enactment. The change in the sexual other triggers an unconscious fantasy about the self and its worth.

The change brought about in the object could be from cold to hot, from demeaned to admired, from high to low, from abandoning to devoted, from hostile to accepting, from resisting to yielding, from insecurely attached to securely attached, from hating to loving, from naughty to nice, from bad to good or good to bad. The change is needed to soothe and inflate the diminished and denigrated self. This may involve appeasing the superego, disguising aggression, bringing love under control, stealing the love, venting sadistic aggression, all variations of release from the oppression of self-esteem. It is the self in conflict with the superego and ego ideal.

In all emotionally meaningful action, the affect follows the change in the object brought about by the action. The affect experienced externally and used as a reality day residue at the center of the elaborated symbolic behavior, produces an affect in response that accompanies the perceptual experience of the change in the day residue in reality. The concept behind that change is unconscious. The percept is conscious. The affect itself is only partially conscious. It is not only feelings in action but action feelings. It is feeling through action. "I do it, then I feel it." Instead of changing feelings about the self so that reality is experienced differently, the attempt is to change reality in order to change feelings about the self. This is true of all symbolic action. The definitional difference of fetish action is the affect of lust and the use of and requirement of reality enactment for progression in the sexual arousal cycle.

The point is: arousal causes a change in the real object representation, therefore a change in the real self-representation and, most importantly, a change in the relational attitude between the two. Attitudinal relationships may be expressed not only physically, with the state change of the body, not only with the act, but most importantly with the change in emotion that accompanies the act and is expressed by the act. This is why the act may be arousing or feared or both.

All normal growth and development to some extent uses reality to change the self. In the healthy aspect of this spectrum is the phenomena we call mastery. But it is done for the pleasure in so doing and for a change in real role function and capacity, and then an emotional identification with that role function and capacity. This then becomes part of the real self. People who are relatively happy with themselves don't wish to change themselves completely and so end up hopefully well integrated mosaics across different developmental phases and role capacities.

Fetish Enactments and Ego Function

Just like in fetish phenomena, fetish enactments occur along a continuum of ego functions and dysfunctions. The same continua apply of necessity, pleasure, reality testing, observing ego, dissociation, in relationship to transitional experiences of growth and development. Because action is required in reality, the basic idea is that these continua, all of them, will depend on how much fantasy has to be not only played out in reality but captures the self's reality experience. This is another way of saying how much has the sexual fantasy captured reality mediating ego functions. Because fetish action is an enactment of the symbolic alteration of reality, whose purpose is to change reality and use an object in reality to change an emotional self-representation experience, the enactment places a strain on reality testing. Can the ego, in spite of the capture of reality during the lustful action, maintain a boundary with reality testing both within the lustful enactment and after, or is there a quasi-delusional or frankly delusional process. Likewise along the require-ment access, not only how rigidly is it required but with what explanation for its requirement and is that explanation delusional. This is the example from the extreme end of the continuum and there are points all along that con-tinuum, to near psychotic, to neurotic, depending on the individual. The nor-mal form is pleasurable sexual action as performance variation, not required for the arousal cycle except for enjoyment and always with the whole person preserved. Part of the pleasure in the normal is that the specific love object is participating.

Fetish Action as Defense

Fetish enactment is used as a defense. It allows discharge of conflicted emo-tional experience. It allows for a compromise between wishes and fears. It is a defense because the sexualization disguises the underlying nonsexual moti-vations and fears. It seems merely sexual and it bypasses the ego defenses of repression and even the anxiety effects of the superego. It suspends observ-ing ego capacity. It enters reality experience directly often with a dissociation of the self. There is a shaping of reality to conform to the fantasy.

If some discordant reality detail enters the scene, it may ruin it and sexual excitement rapidly fades. This is either because the ritual has not been fol-lowed in detail or because it goes too far. This is what is meant by the phrase, "it goes too far." What is meant by it has gone too far is into the feared and warded off danger and no longer can be disguised and so is no longer plea-surable. That which it defends against is suddenly revealed.

The fetish action and lustful affect is a defense against deeper, more upset-ting aspects of warded off object relations and affect concepts. The deeper affect contents involve the wishes and fears that seek compromise in the sexual action.

Sexualization in general and static actions in particular, are attempts at pre-serving attachment in the face of emotional attachment trauma history and present-day difficulties. Its phenomena occur in patients who have insecure attachment. Attachments are colored by fears of abandonment, aggression, unreliability, emotionally parasitizing experiences and entitled attitudes. The normal reliable human attachment bond is replaced by the special fetish action bond in an attempt to preserve a strong attachment via the intense power of sex when love attachment has failed to sustain. Lust is seen as stronger than love.

Fetish Action and Superego

The sexual defense disguises effectively against superego reactions of shame and guilt. But there may then be shame and guilt reactions against the disguise because the disguise is sexual. Sex is to gain permission. The permission is to invent a drama to express love and to see a loving tenderness as well as to vent aggression. It is to feel domination and submission, to feel master and victim and to control and be controlled, that is to say owned; to feel sexual arousal, to reach orgasm, to secure self-esteem safety. Sex allows it because sex disguises everything as just sex. It seems as though it is merely using the other for a sexual, physical gratification. Dumping the whole fantasy into sexual reality serves to defend against and deny the emotional experience of the relationship and the emotional counterreaction of the other. The emotional reaction during the sexual enactment seems reactive not initiative and therefore helps to bypass the superego. But then the superego attack of guilt and shame, diverted from the response against aggression and dominating control, links instead to the sexualization enactment itself.

Shame

Superego attacks of shame and guilt are common in these conditions. Felt acutely as inhibitions and inferiorities outside of sexual arousal, these fears become dissociated during sexual arousal only to return with renewed intensity, because not only is there shame and guilt about qualities of the self but also shame and guilt about the sexual action. It is the shame and guilt layer that forms the dense structure of the neurosis. It isn't only what the self has done but why the self needs to do it and therefore the experience of who the self is. Shame and shame anxiety is the main motivation for dissociation of sexual experience from the experience of personality and self. It becomes a dissociated not me shame experience when not aroused and may be anxiously dissociated when aroused. Disavowal of significance or motive is common.

Shame is in a dynamic relationship between the self, superego and ego ideal. There is a dynamic conflict between the eroticized fetish action and the non-aroused self. Dissociation allows the erotic half of the conflict to function as a determined attempted mastery act undiluted by shame during the arousal cycle. The determination to act is a rebellion against their own shaming ego ideal and the original dissociated humiliation experiences. The sexual enactment is a defiant attempt at shaming of shame itself. This can represent a split ego ideal with a narcissistic, grandiose, powerful, omnipotent arousal fetish ideal and an equally grandiose, punitive, harsh, shaming punishing ego ideal. The ego self-experience identifies with each alternately, depending on the state of arousal. When under the influence of the shaming ideal, the self feels humiliated and sad. When under the influence of the arousal ideal, the self feels euphoric and powerful.

Example

For adults who are aroused by the early pubescent body – a fantasy of sexual inexperience, even innocence – this is a marker of phallic insufficiency and insecurity feelings in the adult. It is easier to feel like a big man or a big woman with the prepubescent. Now there is no fear of being overwhelmed and humiliated by a more sexually experienced partner. Now the adult can feel more secure and confident about their sexual role function. Masturbation fantasies like this can cause shame because they not only seem weak but to enact them is a violation of the law in most parts of the world. These sex fantasies are only hesitantly told because there was a double-edged shame. The need for it is shameful and the fact of it is shameful.

Sex Workers

Sex work has as many motivations and meanings as there are men and women who do this. Often, for the customer, it is a convenient dissociation of the sexual object from the love object, a "Madonna and whore" scenario, especially for any forbidden acts. Then the motivation is to dissociate the shameful desire so as not to contaminate their real-life lover nor reveal themselves as wanting this. The shame is about some shameful act, either sexual or role relational, that the customer dare not ask or do unless it is with a sex worker. This may be in order to spare the self-shame or humiliation.

It is said that buying sex is not about easy in, it's about easy out. But this is also a fantasy; an aspect of the emotional relationship and its roles. The content of those roles may be elaborated, differ from person to person, and when highly erotically charged, may become a fetish enactment with the sex worker, or a sexual act or role as a fetish. The experienced sex worker knows this, and even if not asked, is attuned to it, and goes for it as part of the role performance aspect of their work. They pick up the attitude to them, to sex acts, and the script it implies. If it goes well, it becomes a secret transitional theatre. If done manipulatively and parasitically, it can become a nightmare for the customer. There are some customers who reverse this and attempt to ensnare and parasitize the sex worker, which is the pimp's job. Then comes trouble! That workers need to do sex work to make a living seems sad. This is part of the whole object in reality the customer denies.

Object Relations

The object relations of enacted sexual fantasy are enacted in the relationship to the sexual other. There are different degrees of dissociation between the enacted fantasy and the object in reality, depending on the structure of the ego and depending on the state of arousal. The dissociations, in the mind of the self, play out in behavior to varying degrees at various times.

The fetish action, like a fetish itself, may contain and organize a collection or mosaic of object relations. They are collected within the fetish action or within the fetish object. The attempt at integration occurs in the sexual experience only. Then, for instance, the weaker self can be the stronger self and the perceived strong object can be reduced to the weaker object. Lust is the integrative attempt, albeit in a dissociated state. Lust accomplishes a sexual reversal but still fails at an integration in the self. The degree of integration across various dissociations of the enactment structure in its relationship to personality varies, as does the level of consciousness of that integration or dissociation. There may be a wide disassociation between the dynamics of the sexual enactment and the dynamics of the non-aroused personality. Just such a story is Dr. Jekyll and Mr. Hyde. This is an object relations story.

Another obvious relation story is sex with a stranger. Sex with a stranger, in fantasy or in action, contains sex in the category of the physiological, disassociated from emotional intimacy. With a stranger, there is no commitment to a relationship beyond the sexual. It helps therefore with any shame of frightening but very exciting fantasies of sex, or certain sexual variations. It is a type of compromise formation between the intense desire and the fear. In addition, the past is unknown to the stranger, allowing a role-playing that steps beyond past inhibitions and failures into a new, more exciting acceptance of one's desires.

The etiology is an old argument within psycho analysis. Are the character themes derivative of the dissociated sexual ones or are the sexual themes derivative of the dissociated character ones? Clearly they interact. But it isn't only the etiology of the story, it's the etiology of the dissociation. There is usually the story of attachment trauma and resultant warded off memories of loss, fear, anger and longing.

The fetish action dissociates or separates the sexual from the person of the sexual object and from the person of the nonsexual self. The self and object relationship theme and affect are shifted to the fetish enactment in the sexually aroused state and away from the non-aroused whole person. This is because attachment is represented in sex and is therefore a danger. The danger varies from person to person in its contents and combinations.

Fetish Action and Transitional Processes

Shared fetish enactments allow for the possibility of shared meaning in concordant or concomitant ways that increase sexual pleasure and make possible a transitional experience for both. In a transitional process, both are participant in directing the drama and therefore both can build a mutual enactment that elaborates. The scene is now an interaction that allows for elaboration. This may open the possibility of a development of the major theme and its related sub themes. Development means growth and change.

The shared fetish action means shared secret actions and meanings with their special devotions and special commitment. The commitment is to the scene and its enactment and the commitment to each other is because of it and any deeper commitment is disguised and therefore safe

But telling someone what you want can be a buzz kill. You want them just to know. Because what is exciting is the enactment; specifically, in the tension within the enactment between the known and the unknown, the avoidance and the daring, the not enough and the two much, the hidden and the revealed. The excitement begins with that uncertainty and its exploration. It is in that tension that the excitement lies. The issue is it may not be fully consciously known to either one. And if it is known even to both, it isn't known what the other will participate in nor how much. That is the constantly changing exploratory part of the enactment. If not too rigidly fixed, it can be a shared transitional zone.

How each finds the other and how each come to understand to enact the fantasy is an anxious, exciting part of the fetish enactment. The seduction into it is the beginning of the act. The danger of exposure and shame if not reciprocated, or if shared too quickly, the intensity compulsion that may drive it, all of this is part of the prelude and preliminaries that are actually so much a part of fetish enactments. These constraints and hesitations are on both sides even if it is reciprocated in the sexual fantasy life of each. Each may never discover how close the reciprocity is. It is often closer than they realize, although details are crucial and can be discordant. But the important ones are often surprisingly concordant. The concrete sensory details are where the emotional ideas are displaced, rather than feeling it directly as an emotion and an idea. Therefore, the details of the action are always the excitement and the risk. But in the exploratory preliminaries are the beginning of the object relations story that is the hidden driving force.

Any sharing of growth and development of a sexual enactment increases the intensity of the intimacy bond. It also adds to the trust dangers. What is meant to be secure and to solidify is also a danger and fragile. But it helps the couple feel a special outlier status that intensifies the feeling of specialness to each other and of their relationship. Only they know who each really is sexually because only they know what each really sexually wants. This is the essence of shared sexual enactments whether fetishized or not. What is wanted sexually is easily condensed with the idea of special, deep and true knowing; of what one is, emotionally and in reality.

Being able to use the sex scene flexibly and progressively for growth requires flexible ego functioning where the requirement for sexual performance is not so stereotyped and constricted. There may be flexibility enough outside of that sexual scene to allow for sharing within the relationship that gradually allows for flexibility within the sexual scene that can catalyze growth and development of the relationship and of the two personalities.

Chapter 5

Attachment

We call sex behavior making love with somebody. This tells us that even the ordinary understanding of sexuality is that it is an attachment expression. Sex is not only a noun, a state of being, it is also an action directed to another person. Sex is an attachment story. Love is an attachment phenomena. Lust is a bonding glue. Shared sexual experience is shared emotional experience. All sexual activity, alone or with another, in fantasy or reality, is a relationship. The beginning, middle and end of sexual activity, in behavior and in fantasy, tends to tell the story of that relationship. The name for the feeling of being involved in a relationship is the word attachment. Sex is a form of attachment. Sex tells the story of attachment needs and fears. "Will you be mine" is a story about a type of attachment. Sex tells the object relations story of attachment. Sex can be used casually or ironically but this also reveals the nature of the relationship.

One of the ways this attachment relationship is experienced is through the sensory-emotional experience of sexual activity. As a previous chapter showed, lustful sensuality is very stimulating, not just of the sexual emotions but of all emotions. This chapter discusses relationship emotions represented in sensuous emotional experience. Sensory experience readily kindles meaning and contains crucial emotional aspects of the sexual attachment story. Sensory emotional sensual details are metaphors of emotional experience, especially relationship meaning and the attachment experiences at their core.

All human sexual experience and fantasies usually involve touching and connections because sex is an inter-physical experience. This makes it the ideal representation for interpersonal attachment experiences and relationships. It also makes it an ideal experience for gratification of attachment needs but also for the perils of attachment insecurities and ambivalences. The attitudes to attachment, basic to personality, are pictured in the sexual scene. The deeper meanings and psychological conflicts are often revealed in the meanings of the sensory experience.

The physical sensation of the child to the attachment object is through all sensory modalities: the voice, the appearance, the smell, the physical feel. Later, when the needed other is experienced also through human sexuality,

DOI: 10.4324/9780429491733-6

with a very powerful immediate positive reinforcement of lust affect and orgasm, it becomes a natural venue for the re-experiencing of these sensory manifestation memories of attachment. The quickest way to reproduce the physical experience of caregiving and care receiving is in the actual, adult experience of physicality. This can be hand holding, physical touch, or gentle kissing, but because those expressions are undisguised expressions of attachment bonding, those with anxieties and ambivalence about it may seek the expression and reception of tender interchange through another major physical experience of adult sharing, which is sex. There, because of the sexual disguise, a man or woman can feel powerful yet experience the tender. The man can feel he is on top of the relationship. A woman can feel that the man is her sexual slave. On top, or on bottom as sexual slave, are terms that refer to the emotional relationship and the quality and needs of the attachment bond.

The need to experience the psychological in the real, the attachment desire needing a physical act, is an overarching issue in the psychology of sexual experience but perhaps particularly so when attachment and dependency needs are both intense and ambivalent.

Attachment in preverbal children and their caregivers is expressed physically. There is tone of voice, there is gesture, there is attention, but there is also holding, kissing, stroking and soothing. The issue is physical touch and what it is used to convey, in this case, a strong and loving emotional attachment. The attachment story is told not in what is done but in the experience of what is done; in the emotional meaning of what is done, in the attitude toward what is done and to the those who are doing.

Sensory experiences are stimuli in reality that can be used to strengthen the experience of the real object. The real object is an internal self-experience of the perceived real other. Sexual experience harkens back to the earliest attachment phenomena in the infant, which is heavily sensory: touch, smell, taste, vision, hearing. The sensory experiences are part of the core curiosity experience and emotional fantasy of attachment to and meaning of a real object. That it is the body in reality and the real object strengthens the idea about motive in attachment and the behavior reflecting early attachment needs and ambivalences. It is about survival. The infant forms the strength of its attachment to the entire sensory emotional experience of the real attachment object. It makes the sensory experience of human sexuality a core feature of the attachment fantasy aspects of sexual experience.

You can see this in all sexual fantasy or sexual relationships. They are contained within the package of the attachment to the other person. Those attachments may be clinging, negligent, attacking, tracking, avoidance, but they are attachments. They are related to the larger issue of attachment and to being secure or insecure or something in between or something mixed.

When there is an intense, anxious attachment need and a shift to sensory emotional thing presentation attachment experience, sex may be intense.

This is because the attachment experience by the child is a multisensory experience of familiarity and consistency. Mom and dad always smell the same way. When parental emotions and behavior are erratic and unstable, their physicality becomes the target of constant and reliable connection. That doesn't change.

A man fell in love with what he felt was his lover's perfect body. The details of why that body is perfect will tell us about his emotional requirements for his ideal object of attachment. The anatomical details and their meaning to him will reveal the emotional attributes he seeks in his object of attachment. That he finds her personality difficult is his repetition compulsion, another sign of anxious attachment. He is trying to master his anxious attachment to a difficult object, seeking emotional security in physical aesthetics.

Other adult forms of insecure sexual attachments are the memori morti and memori vita of meaningful reality memento objects and rituals symbolizing, the past. Sometimes they are called linking objects but there are also linking enactments and relationships. They are found throughout culture and religion. They all have to do with object permanence and object constancy and with attachment to the object in reality and the strength of the real object's constancy. Often the original trauma was not object permanence but object constancy, symbolically represented by permanence. They increase a wish for the infinite object. When there is attachment deprivation and insecurity, Winnicott points out that there is a shift from the environment (relational) mother to the object (body) mother. This is an aspect of what he meant. The shift may involve the sexual body.

Attachment always has issues of permanence, reciprocity, traumas both acute and strain, grandiose wishes and fears. Love is always complicated because of the reality of the independent emotional life of a dependency object. When in tune at the moment of need it is wonderful. When it is not, it is disappointing and may be frightening. When it is lost in childhood, it is devastating. For some, the moment of mutual attachment is a trigger for danger.

There are many neurotic problems with which attachment must reckon. They have to do with someone's neurotic relationships to attachment. These problems are disguised and symbolically represented in the sensory details and sex acts they find most exciting. Sex allows for a controlled and hidden attachment plot. The details are preformed by the attitudinal organization of the personality themes of attachment.

Neurotic forms of attachment can take some classic forms. One can see this played out dramatically in sexual behavior and fantasies that show the relationship to the desired object disguised as the relationship to the object of desire. Those relationships have certain themes or stories. When stereotyped and fixed, the relationships are neurotic and reveal a characteristic personality adaptation for neurotic problems of attachment.

These neurotic dynamics play themselves out not only by attaching to the sensory experience of sex, but by the whole relationship to the sexual object. One such attachment is to the unavailable object. The relationship to an unavailable object has many variations on the theme: attachment to the one who got away, attachment to the one who has yet to come, attachment to the dissociated object, attachment to the addiction object, attachment to the unreliable object, attachment to the overheated object, attachment to the cold object, attachment to the frightened frozen object, attachment to the angry object, attachment to the duplicitous object, the object of betrayal. Even though all are masochistic objects of desire, all are also ideal objects, aggrandized or debased, or both.

These attachment issues are most obvious in commitment problems. They take the form of failures to commit, instantaneous commitment, commitment to the body but not to the person, angry commitments and passive commitments. There are infinite manifestations and variations.

One classic is the continuing attachment to the one who got away. There is continued mourning over the loss, which is never complete because the sufferer never relinquishes the bond of hope. Attachment is never fully over and therefore is not yet ready to be mourned. There is an idealization of the past that serves to deny the ambivalence of the past and the continuing problem with ambivalence in the present. Attachment relationships with such people tend to be highly ambivalent and their tolerance of their ambivalence is not strong. Therefore they attack, dilute, avoid, diminish, or sever the relationship, which they later then regret and mourn. The lost one becomes a lost ideal and their relationship to their own ego ideal is often a longing to fulfill what is a grandiose expectation of themselves and of life with the feeling of defeat and inferiority constant because they can't match their own unreasonable expectations, all of which were supposed to overcome their feelings of defeat and inferiority stemming from their childhood relationships.

All these dynamics are often disguised but obvious in their sensory experience of the sexual object's unique and therefore special anatomic specificity. Because these details can't be duplicated in anyone else, they feel they will never find anyone else. That they have invested these qualities with the meaning of specialness and uniqueness and could do so with someone else does not occur to them because they don't experience it that way. They feel that their feelings of attachment to the anatomic specifics are a quality of the sexual object's anatomy and not of their own emotional investment in it.

In this, are aspects of a fetish, the intense valuation of a part of the anatomy as the thing itself. Fetishistic interest in anatomy, to the exclusion of the ambivalently held person, is the other feature of fetish in some attachment problems. There is a disassociation between the body and the person, between sex and the rest of the relationship. In this, there is an intense, romantic, idealized purity in the anatomic, and a denigrated hostility in the relationship to the person. In treatment, one can always show them that some of the anatomical specificity was revealed to them after a feeling of attachment and not before. One can also show that prior attachment feeling was to the person and the person's presentation of self, which has some of the qualities of the anatomic detail they are so attracted to.

Example

A young man loses his intensely appealing lover and finds himself missing a particular aspect of her anatomy. She had very pink soft nipples that he loved to look at. He was in love with the aesthetic pleasure he found there. He felt in love with her nipples. No other nipples would do. The key to its meaning was in the use of his term "admire." He admired them. He thought they were perfect. He thought they were nature's special artistic creation. It felt like nature's gift to him, special to him, because he could appreciate and admire them. He recalled that old saying that the Devine and the artist are in a conversation and it's best for the artist to say as little as possible. This perfectly expressed his special relationship with the object and not the person. He was an artist because of his Devine artistic appreciation of them and looked upon their perfection as Devine. That was his relationship to the special, to the unique, to the infinite aesthetic, and the wished-for transformational relationship with it. With access to those nipples, he felt in possession of what he needed for a profound feeling of acceptance and relationship to loving goodness, the ultimate relationship to the Devine. Of note is the disassociation from her as a person. She always made it clear how turned on to him she was. She also always made it clear that she was married and would never leave her husband and children. She was inhibited in ambition but not sex. He was inhibited in sex but not ambition. She participated sexually in his ambition. He participated sexually in her admiration.

What they don't feel secure in is that the feeling of special uniqueness that they crave would be experienced in the special and unique relationship they could have with the other person. That they don't understand this is often because they haven't experienced that in childhood with their primary love objects. They did not experience being special and unique to their love object in childhood because that love object did not have the capacity to experience them in that way. But they fear it is they who can't be loved in that way and seek to prove that they can be. By giving to the other what they themselves seek. They then prove to themselves that they are worthy of receiving it. But unfortunately, they have already transferred their primary attachment from the person to the physical body.

This is because the physical body has object permanence and constancy. Its physical constancy is reassuring against the anxiety of emotional inconstancy in the woman. A woman's moods change and her affection may be fleeting. Her nipples never change, except with excitement; excitement for him. Unmentioned are the changes that come with parturition and age. These may be frightening to contemplate because it awakens the original abandonment trauma where feelings and relationships changed – for the worse.

A very similar dynamic plays out in the fantasy of the one who has yet to come. There is a number 10 out of 10 always waiting to be found just beyond the horizon. That is the one who will rescue the seeker from a history of failures and anxiety about impossibility. That is the one who will rescue the seeker from their lonely exile from love. They don't realize that the problem is in the self's ability to love others. This love ability has been damaged perhaps because of trauma linking loving to humiliation and loss of self-esteem.

Sufferers from this dynamic have similar self-esteem problems as the one suffering from the one who got away. They hope that an ideal object will take the place of their own ego ideal and help them feel good about themselves because their external ideal feels good about them. A very nice solution if one can find it, but in practice often even when the ideal object finds them and approves of them, they then start to denigrate the object. The "oh wow" becomes the "oh ugh." If sexualized, this takes the form of the sudden discovery of an anatomic flaw that is a turn off. This tends to happen as they start to feel a possibility of attachment, for which they hate, fear and desperately yearn.

For those who are frightened of attachment, there can sometimes be the adaptation of attachment to a dissociated object. If sexualized, it takes the form of an intense sexual relationship with someone who is not integrated into the life of either. The classic sexualized situation illustrating this dynamic is the extramarital affair where the lover is the sexual object. Because of the strength of the sexual attachment, the attachment anxieties are also very high there but there is also the strong feeling of attachment in the sexual attraction. The dissociation is usually from a companion object with whom there is a trustworthy attachment but without excitement. This is because sexual excitement with the intimate object would introduce the instability of attachment that comes with intense desire, that is to say, intense need, that is warded off and disassociated.

In the attachment to the sexually exciting lover, aspects of her body are often emotionally meaningful sensuous details. They are experiencing presentations in reality. In the preceding example of nipples, their symbolic significance is a good example. The addicted to the others body person doesn't experience the symbolic representation or aspect of the object in reality because it is an object in reality and they really are pink nipples. This is used to disavow their emotional significance.

These attachments to the sensuous body of the other are displacements and reparations for the difficulties and ambivalence in attachment through the relationship with the other. It can result not only in intensities but in inhibitions. Inhibitions of orgasm may involve the feeling that since the reliable attachment is for sexual excitement, orgasm ends the sexual excitement and therefore ends the strength of the attachment. The goal then is to delay or avoid that moment of reckoning that is a moment both of intense physical satisfaction and of intense feelings of loss.

Any of these attachments may be felt with a force that is like an addiction. Now the anxiety of loss is conscious and the ambivalence due to the fear of that loss is a suffering. They cannot get enough and they cannot let go. Depending on ego function, the addicted can be driven to extremes. This is because the addiction label describes an intensity of demand that can be quite irrational and never sated, or only briefly, and as soon as it is temporarily sated it becomes repulsive. This irrational conundrum has to do not with the intensity of the feelings but rather with the impossibility for their lasting gratification in reality. There is a compulsive quality to addiction that pushes it into behavior that can be quite demanding. Depending on ego function, it can also be dangerous. These addictions are on a continuum of neurotic, near psychotic and frankly delusional. When infiltrated with resentment, rage, jealousy and vengeance, they can be dangerous. The therapeutic approach is to point out the mixture of hatred with the supposed love feelings. But the very ill can acknowledge this but claim it is justified. The therapeutic approach is to perhaps then show them that what they fear ultimately has just happened in that if their claim is justified then their love is bogus.

Addiction to the object can be particularly painful when the object is always unreliable. One type of unreliability is when the object is only intermittently available. Then there is a saturation and an alternating longing. There is a back-and-forth, on-again off-again that reinforces the addiction, as only a randomly reinforced stimulus can do. It is one of the most powerful reinforcement forms a positive stimulus has. In addiction the sufferer cannot get enough of the object of addiction. After a momentary saturation, and sometime after that point a repulsion, then the longing begins again.

Some of these addictive objects are in fact unavailable. Their very unavailability is a hidden attraction to those with ambivalent attachment problems. Then the longing can be pure without the ambivalence because the object is never in reality a possible attachment. Then, the ambivalence is in the object not in the self. The self can feel secure in an ambivalent love because real attachment and commitment is impossible due to the ambivalence in the object. Any treatment of this condition must explore the underlying ambivalence about any attachment to a stable and available love object of any sort in the self.

One type of addictive attachment is the obsessive, frozen person who longs for a heated lover. The heated sexual other is to provide the excitement and the evocation of affect that the seeker has trouble feeling themselves. Then comes the failure to respond adequately to the heated lover's emotional needs. Then comes the change of the sexually hot lover into the heated angry lover. Now the unfeeling partner is frightened and withdraws, intensifying the anger.

Some are attracted to the always angry object. Anger is seen as a brave assertion of self against the oppressive forces of society; of convention, of commitment itself. The inhibited one feels reassured in the angry one's presence. They hope to be allied in a loving peace with the angry, strong one. But more often, sooner or later, they find themselves the target of the anger, like everyone else. Now comes the misery of a felt rejection. Now the opportunity to exercise the personality defenses of either counterattack or masochistic pleading. Either may kindle more anger and more fighting, or forgiveness and reconciliation. This usually proves to be temporary because with peace may come intimacy feelings which trigger an excuse to be angry again. Then they are off on another round.

Perhaps the most woeful is the attachment to the object of betrayal. There are those who fall in love with people who like to betray the very attachment they seduce. For those so addicted, hope turns into despair over and over. They can't understand it because it seems to be going so well. They never understand that going so well is the trigger for the betrayal. The betrayal wouldn't hurt unless it was at first going well. It isn't fun to squash a sandcastle that hasn't yet been built.

All of these addictions are addictive attachments to what many would find negatively reinforcing objects. The negative reinforcing object is the conundrum of psychotherapy but the delight of psychoanalysis. Only ambivalence can explain it. Only conflict can explain it. They betray the masochistic nature of the seeker of these delights. Often with insecure attachment, severe superegos, low self-esteem and ambitions to conquer the desire of the other instead of conquering their own insecurity, they seek the difficult and not the easy. If they should ever win the unconditional love of the withholding or abusive object, they cry because the fight for love is a stalemated mourning over the loss of love or a never available love.

It's a fight for the self-esteem worth of a victim who feels they can only be healed by a successful conquest of the unwilling. They feel that to partner with a loving partner would deny them the victory of the conquest. It is vengeance through love and success that they seek and a substitute for the fight, even the loving object they crave but had without a fight is no decent substitute. They have an unconscious angry ambition that will not be satisfied until a love victory is had. Those addicted to this process will seek another love to conquer if the one they are involved in too easily yields. This is a continuation of the love trauma where they felt they had to fight for love and therefore for their self-esteem but felt they lost or that it was a stalemate.

Fetish things provide controllable, stable object attachments instead of attachment to the unstable emotional life of another person.

Fetish enactment is a sexualized wished-for, reassuringly fixed, type of emotional object relationship. The lust excitement to the stereotypy is the reassuring sexualized intensity defense against the feared lack of stable, predictable attachment from the object of dependency. Because human emotion is changeable, they fear change. They can tolerate some attachment but only in the reassuringly inanimate form of a fetish or the stereotyped fetish enactment. Attachment is to the specific lustful sensory details that the sexual act always provides.

Many men enjoy the blow job and for some it has special meaning, fetishized meaning. It can have similar special meaning for the woman. The sensation of interest to the man is often the firmness of the hold, the gentleness of the tongue stroking, which approximates a soothing. The partner swallowing of semen may be a fantasy of being admired, wanted, so much as to be irresistibly taken in and safely, permanently held in the stomach-heart. The man can feel the attachment dependency need gratified while at the same time feeling strong and dominant. This is a quick fix for attachment ambivalence in which perhaps the man, when a boy, felt weak and bullied by a strong but emotionally unreliable mother. Dependency needs now make him feel weak and denigrated.

Note that this is only one possibility in one human being. There are infinite other possibilities of meaning for any sexual act, including the possibility that it's merely a fun thing to do. The meaning will begin to be revealed when the man tells the story of the blow job, what feels so good about it, and what the meaning is of that which feels so good. For those for whom it has a meaning, even a special meaning, the story of that meaning can reveal basic personality issues that are more disguised when expressed in other ways. It can be hard to see the dependency needs in a physically powerful man who may be defended against tenderness. Sex may be the one place he feels safe enough to experience it. He may never express to her the value he places on the act because he fights awareness of that liking which reveals to him his own experience of vulnerability. He may only know that he likes it and wants it and the times, when unconsciously feeling vulnerable, he needs it and demands it. Then he feels repaired from his weakness by his assertive demand and his fantasy of her yielding to him out of passionate attachment to him.

Another example is the butt and the idealized potential of turning shitty aspects of judgmental rejection by the love object into the gold of love and appreciation. There is idealization as a defense against and transformation of the rejecting and the denigrating. It turns repulsion and avoidance by the fantasized rejecting object into excited pleasure and action, thereby preserving the attachment bond. It is a triumphant transformation.

All orgasm has some element of triumph and transformation because of the changes in the body required and the satisfaction upon reaching the goal, but for some people, the dynamics of their self-esteem is specifically linked to the transformation feelings of orgasm. They sadly don't have such feelings in their relationships. They don't have orgasms of acceptance and love and tenderness in the relationship because of who they fear they are and their emotional value to another person, and perhaps also because of their object choice, the rejecting or abusive person.

These examples are examples of the fetishized use of bodies and people. Fetishized means not only displaced to a thing or an action, but displaced into reality. The fetish is an object in reality. The fetish action is an action with people in reality. The symbolic uses and symbolic alterations of reality are for the purpose of validating a wished for emotional state of the self. It is a projection of the self's emotional feelings about the self onto the reality sexual object of the other person's body.

The need for a reality object with which to enact again speaks to the attachment aspect of the phenomena. The need for reality, addiction to reality, as opposed to the emotional meaning of reality, is a measure of their emotional deprivation in reality as children. It is felt in their real self-experience because they feel they really were abused and or deprived. Reality then provides stimulation for the exteroceptive sensory system and the sensory experience of reality which validates the emotional. The enactment is intense, recruits the relevant emotions, disguises the origins and complexity of feelings in the sensory experience, and in the change forced upon reality. This is almost as good as fixing the past reality because it fixes the present feelings about reality. It fixes temporarily the living, in the present, in the moment, reality echo of the past. For the emotionally hungry, who fear repetition of trauma, this is the best they can do. Psychoanalysis offers them the opportunity to understand the emotional present and its link to the emotional past so that they can resolve it better in the present and no longer need to cling to the symbolic representation and the repetition in present reality. They then can really have what they want which is a loving emotional relationship with another person now in reality.

Personality and personality defense is clearly seen in attachment styles. These attachment styles try to gratify both the wish for closeness and the fear of it in a way that reassures. These ways differ depending on personality type.

The paranoid personality has a suspicious attachment style which is both overly cautious and can abruptly be overly trusting. When disappointed, it seems to them as though their original suspicion was justified. The analytic literature says that they are projecting and while this is true, it is often most available in treatment as a projection from their object representation not their self-representation. They are projecting to the object in reality an emotional experience of objects and acting according to the projection. The process of enacting the reaction to their own projection is common in all personality disorders, especially the more severe. The content of suspiciousness is the characteristic of the paranoid personality. Paranoid personality is constantly seeking a safe place and a safe time for sex. Nudity risks the feeling of exposure. Secluded places and darkness can be reassuring as is the unique sexual flourish or focus that avoids competition. Their choice of sexual partner may involve the superficially common but the secretly interior special. This is the Clark Kent exterior and the Superman interior. This is the librarian exterior and sexual cauldron interior. This is the ice king or ice queen exterior with the warm, loving acceptance interior and only for the paranoid lover. Only the paranoid person knows the secret inside. Then their loved one is safe from the competitive and envious eyes of others. Then they are safe themselves from competitive attack. The secret interior may be symbolically represented by the sensory emotional experience of an anatomical site that is especially prized and especially erotic.

Histrionic personalities tend to project a romantic glow and emotionality onto the attachment relationship. It is a fantasy of a mutually connecting idealization of the romantic relationship. Any discord or misunderstanding can bring angry tears of disappointment and recriminations about not being loved. The loving attachment is a perfectly symbiotic one according to them. Difference threatens their romantic fantasy of union, where two people are united in devotional commitment to the romantic attachment. Their attachment style tends to be an instantaneous commitment, which is to the intense emotion they feel, not to the object of the emotion, except secondarily. They want marriage, as a symbol of romantic commitment, not necessarily the particular other. Histrionic personalities come in male and female varieties, the male form often overlooked in Western culture.

An extreme version of the histrionic personality is the infantile personality who acts like a four-year-old histrionic in their demands for attention and for physical objects of value. All their wants are experienced as needs and all attachments are transaction possibilities for need gratification. Dramatic angry emotional displays accompany disappointment.

In all, insecure attachment characteristic of each personality type, may trigger the need to control. The spectrum of ego function pathology is shown in the variation of how extreme this need is.

The obsessive thinks it is the facts they are trying to control. They don't realize it is the control they are trying to control. Because orgasm involves a controlled being out of control, and some spontaneity, which is threatening to the psychological balance of the obsessive, sex tends to be ritualized. This was explained in a popular movie when the female character, complaining to her obsessive boyfriend about this style of lovemaking, said it was always: "Titty titty titty titty pooooosy; titty titty titty titty pooooosy." Boring, she said. To break that sequence, that ritualized sequence, is to release the anxiety of performance perfection and in the male, can cause loss of erection. Women too may have these rituals. They commonly present as precoital cleanliness rituals or precoital withholdings or fights.

The narcissistic attachment has to do with a grandiosity of the self and acceptance by the object of that grandiosity. The adoration they seek in attachment is the adoration of their grandiose self in the fantasy that this is or soon will be the real self. Any discordance in the continuous background enactment of that fantasy brings disappointment and an intense rage. When sexualized, it may take the form of a sensory emotional performance experience of perfection as an enhancement to the narcissistic self. For the sexual object to assert dominance over that special performance can trigger the narcissistic rage.

The sadomasochistic personality attaches strongly with domination and submissive suffering as their form of love. The sadistic self makes the masochistic object miserable and the loving masochistic object accepts this contract in order to feel they are about to be loved. The sadistic self does this to the masochistic object in order to feel powerful with vengeful forces directed against crimes committed against them as children. That this can be a strong form of attachment is seen over and over again in the tumultuously stormy yet infinitely enduring nature of many of these relationships. The pain inflicted may be physical and sexualized but more often it is emotional and not sexualized. But when it is sexualized, it can lead to painful sexual enactments that may be intensely erotic for the participants but also intensely sad. Mild forms such as erotic pinches and smacks are common. Their meaning is usually disavowed.

All these examples are examples of the need to emotionally alter and use the altered real object and its sensory qualities. These alterations are on an ego function continuum of normal, neurotic, near psychotic, or psychotic. The distinction involves not just the feelings about the real object but how conscious or unconscious the alteration is perceived and the associated reality testing. Reality testing is the ability to understand what is inherent in the object in reality and what is one's own emotional experience.

The sociopath betrays attachment as a defense against having felt attachment betrayal in childhood. They were the victim of emotionally parasitizing and betrayal of their emotional needs. Whenever attachment feelings solidify, they betray. The feelings could be either in the object of attachment or in themselves.

The other way that attachment problems may be represented in human sexuality is in their effect on the arousal cycle. Inhibitions or abruptions in process through the cycle may be the result of their symbolic representational experience. Orgasm delay in men and women may represent a phobic avoidance of the rush of strong attachment feelings that ensues. Because these attachments feelings are insecure and signal impending terrible feelings of rejection and loss, the orgasm experience may be avoided. Each step in the arousal cycle has the potential to signify a dysphoric fantasy about attachment. Often the content of the fantasy is unconscious but not the affect. It is one reason for a post-orgastic dysphoria. In order to get the fantasy content, the analyst focuses on the affect.

Chapter 6

Masturbation

Masturbation is the sexual stimulation of the self, usually to orgasm. It is usually accompanied by fantasy. Masturbation fantasy is an imaginative story the self tells to the self. It is ostensibly just about sex. But it is also about the sexual self in relationship to sexual others. That means it is basically about the relationship to others, sexual and nonsexual. Arousal, sexual sensations, attitudes, and their stories express deepest relationship wishes and fears. What the story is about is how to achieve emotional satisfaction not just sexual satisfaction. It is a story about how to use sexual satisfaction for emotional satisfaction.

Its advantage over sex in reality is that the events and sequences, the pace and the reactions, the object other and the self and their relationship, are all totally under control of the self. The disadvantage is that it still isn't clear what it actually means. In this sense, it is like a sexual dream. The sex, because of its intensity, tends to overpower and disguise the other, nonsexual emotional meanings in the masturbation fantasy or dream. But that gives a chance, because of the disguise of sex, for basic personality problems, wishes, fears and personality adaptations to be clearly portrayed in the disguise of sex.

A masturbation fantasy uses imagined reality as a vehicle. The qualities of reality experience are used to validate the fantasy as a wished for experience and as a hoped for real experience. The reality is of sensory qualities, especially when intensely organized as a thing presentation. A thing presentation recruits reality to validate fantasy wishes. The fantasy uses sensory-emotion of the aroused body in reality. This is the form of the representations that are sexual thing presentations. Thing presentation experience is a package bypassing the superego because it is experienced as presented rather than built. It doesn't seem constructed nor voluntary. In the relationship to the self, the thing presentation is an other. There is shame about it but there is less responsibility for it than an action in reality. In addition, because it intensifies the sensory, it disguises the emotional, another way it bypasses the superego, at least in the aroused state. Therefore, in the aroused state there is a different structural relationship of the mental agencies. The ego self in the aroused state has suspended doubt and therefore some insecurity.

DOI: 10.4324/9780429491733-7

We tend to think that masturbation is about sex. It's not. It's about a person's relationship with other people and themselves. It's about personality needs and fears. Sexual needs are also emotional needs and express all the emotional wishes and fears contained within a person.

It is common in both men and women, and in most age groups, sometimes even before mature orgasm is possible. It is usually accompanied by fantasy. The fantasy depicts some sexual encounter in imagined reality. The fantasy is usually a sequence of images that tell a story. The story is ostensibly about what is done and where on the body it is done. The psychological story has to do with to whom it is done and why it is done. This deeper story of meaning and motivation has elements that are readily apparent on the surface of the manifest content of the story. To see it clearly, one has to not be distracted by the sexually exciting aspects and focus on the human story of self and object that is so clearly displayed.

Masturbation is a conversation with oneself about the sexual body self, the sexual body of the other and the relationship between the two. It is therefore an object relations story. This story is primarily about self-states, self-esteem, and its vicissitudes in relationship to primary significantly held others. It therefore has within its story, the story of formative, past object relations in the history of attachment and self-esteem issues. The story has present day frustrations and triggers to excitement. The story has a wished for route to self-esteem success. The story has a delineation of the role function of self and other that can achieve self-esteem enhancement.

Stable sexual fantasy, if there is one, is called a core masturbation fantasy or sex print which is characteristic of the person. It is a stereotyped, singular or close cluster, of symbolic representation series whose details link to the arousal cycle. It tells a constantly repeating story, with different variations, that describe the different meanings and themes and their aspects. The masturbation fantasy shows not only the wished for sexual actions but also their linked wished for emotional self-states and wished for emotional object states. The fantasy thus reveals core personality themes. The masturbation fantasy is a core personality fantasy that is sexualized. Core personality dynamic fantasies are wished-for self and object relationship states.

An important issue is whether the story is deadlocked or whether it is developing. Developing does not necessarily mean a change in the basic plot but rather in the elaboration of details that slowly reveals, over time, over growth and development of the individual, the deeper plot, which first appears in consciousness as a story about the other but at deeper layers is also about the self. Masturbation often has a self-state that changes from yearning to satisfied. What is the self-esteem in the yearning state and what is it in the satisfied state? What has to happen in the sexual scene and in the object to make this change? What is the exciting required action and what does that required action represent psychologically? It isn't just a sexy story. It is a personality meaning story.

These are the questions to which the analytic method can help provide answers. They are answers about the elaborated story and its meta-themes of attachment and self-esteem. They are answers about deep motivations and fears in the object relations of attachment that are profoundly true about the person in their real life relationships, sexual and nonsexual. These emotional themes may be more disguised in their real relationships.

Because there are various defenses in functioning personality, defenses of repression, reversal, projection and dissociation, the masturbation fantasy can be extremely helpful in revealing a less defended story about motivational and anxiety plot motivations and their object relations manifestations. The first step is to understand that sex is a vehicle for emotional satisfaction and a compelling, distracting disguise of it. The key to interpreting is focusing on the relationships pictured in the fantasy sex acts, and the meaning of sex to the person who is doing the fantasizing.

Masturbation fantasy has a certain structure or arrangement. The most important is the arrangement linking the sensory experience of the sexual body self to the sexual body other. There are the emotions about the self and the other and their relationship. These crucial emotions are experienced as being revealed in the physical changes of the two bodies as they progress through the arousal cycle. The story is linked to certain intensely arousing details. The details are anatomic and physiologic arousal levers triggering sensory affect, often of an intensity that triggers thing presentation experience and structure. It is also in the themes of the story as it progresses during the fantasy. To decode the manifest themes, explore what the self feels about themselves and the objects, and what the object feels about themselves and the other, as the story progresses. It is feelings about the self and object relationship during those acts which the acts themselves represent. The themes can be translated into words and affect concepts from the lustful sensory experience of the sexual sensory details.

Specially meaningful details are points in the arousal cycle in which the next phase is activated. These arousal details are filled with meaning and can be called nodes. These nodes tend to be thing presentations in which the intense sensory experience is filled with emotional meanings that seem to be a quality of the physical detail of the sexual body of the other rather than emotional meanings in the mind of the self. The arousal nodes, joining with fantasy, create and express fantasy nodes of highly condensed eroticized psychodynamics. Fantasy now is expressed as a physical sensory emotional erotic thing presentation experience sequence but consciously seems to be merely a lustful physical experience. Sequenced, the TPs form a story, and the story is about the motivations for, fears of and satisfactions in the relationship experience, which is the context in which the sexual fantasy acts occur.

It has strong reality qualities given to the fantasy by the sensory emotional system as it is aroused by real physical details. Because masturbation is occurring with a real body of the self, just as the active fantasy is occurring with the real body of the other, they use reality sensual experience both as levers of enhancement of fantasy and as validators of its truth value.

Screen Memory

The structure of the experience is like a screen memory. The structure of a screen memory is a stereotyped memory with intense sensory emotion and fixed story, experienced as reality and using reality sensory memory experience for the experience of emotional meaning. The screen memories may or may not be veridical, but exactly true or not, are preserved in status nascendi; fixed in the process of becoming. They remain frozen in memory, unchanged yet charged with meaning feeling that never appears. Therefore the memory is frozen without any process to elaborate and explain. It is filled with emotional reactions because it contains within it intense emotional condensations of meanings that are emotionally painful. The person experiencing the memory feels that the memory is maintained because it is such a powerful reality event. But it is also maintained because it expresses powerful emotional feelings and meanings to which reality qualities not only verify but obfuscate. The obfuscation is in the reality, which seems so powerful that it provides a reality meaning rather than the emotional meaning the person brings to the reality, assembles the screen memory with, and re-experiences it. The diagnosis of screen memory is made on its surface because of its intensity and recurrence and mainly by its stereotypy; its unchanging nature, the fact that there are no added main or even peripheral details. It is a scene frozen in time. It often reflects core personality emotional themes and defenses. The screen memory harnesses a reality event of the past for use as a symbolic representation now, of important personality themes. It can therefore include in the condensation other similarly themed events. The condensation illustrates the emotional themes and variations on those themes that were stirred by the event.

Masturbation fantasy may be like a screen memory in its structure, if there are memory icons and if it is stereotyped and unchanging. It has the same reality experience aspects, the same relationship of emotional meaning to reality, the same temptation to use reality for validation of emotional meaning, the same acceleration of emotional meaning in the sensory system, and the same resistance to change lest hidden anxious meanings be revealed.

Over time, non-neurotic masturbation fantasy tends to slowly grow and develop if the person is growing and developing. It can change dramatically when there is a reality event that dramatically changes the person's self-esteem, for better or worse. The history of the masturbation fantasy is therefore a history of the growth and development of the person, of the ego and its defenses and its growth and development vicissitudes. The fantasy may adapt to reality challenges and to self-esteem changes. During growth and development of the life cycle and personality, the fantasy reflects either a healthy result of healthy progression in the life cycle or as consolation for failure or frustration. Often it is both.

The masturbation fantasy can change from incidence to incidence in its particulars, according to different self-states; different states of self-esteem. These self-states are linked to reality happenings and non-happenings, to successes and failures, to derivative wished-fors and feareds. These self-state changes will be reflected in the compulsivity of occurrences and hopefully in the particular iterations of the core story. Patients are usually not aware of these links to their actual lives. Masturbation, seemingly about sexual actions and sexual others, is also and primarily about the state and reality vicissitudes of the self-esteem.

The need to use reality for validation of the emotional is the idea that because it really happened, therefore, the emotional reaction is valid. While true, it elides the point that if validation is necessary for emotional reactions then there is some conflict about the emotional reaction which should need no validation other than its existence as a feeling. Meaningful to me should need no validation. It might need explanation, but not validation. It can be useful and adaptive but that is a different meaning of the word valid. This would be the meaning of practical rather than ethical. It would be the meaning of useful rather than the meaning of morally good. This doesn't mean it would be morally bad only that the two are different. The role of feeling is to provide meaning and that comes from the self. Reality validation is a major motivator for human sexual experience including masturbation. This mechanism is a major human adaptation. It is one motivator for the symbolic alteration of reality powering the creative use of changes in reality for adaptational mastery.

Where fantasy and arousal meet and join, each catalyzes the other. The arousal nodes, joining with fantasy, and the reality of the aroused body, create and express fantasy nodes of highly condensed eroticized psychodynamics. Once again, it isn't the what or the how but rather the who and the why.

The masturbation fantasy is where the personality dynamics are usually clearest because it, unlike in unaroused reality, even with reality enactments, reality is never exactly the fantasy. In masturbation, the core personality fantasy is not limited by reality and can more clearly reveals its truth to itself.

Thus we see that masturbation isn't primarily about physical sex. It's about the fantasy and the use of the real body for the purpose of expressing and validating the fantasy; its emotional experience. In the human being, sexual experience is as much about emotional experience as it is about drive discharge, procreation, or the sensory pleasure. Even those for whom it is merely about sport, sex has that important meaning in their own dynamic psychology. Life is just fun. Relationships are just transactional.

Because the fantasy is controllable in every detail, and because it is about physical attachment and inter action, it can express emotional attachment. It can show the complicated emotions, self-states and relationships of attachment that are motivating and conflicted. Wishes and fears can together be synthesized. The synthesis can be better expressed and satisfied, for the moment, as sexual because the sexual lust disguises, even as it contains, all the other affect and affect ideas that constitute self and object experience and their relationship to each other. The plot, hidden in all these sensory emotional details, can succeed in sequencing all its elements and therefore in its conclusion.

The sequence is important because it tells a story. The story has a beginning, middle and end. It has an after end. Thus we see that. Now I am, for a while, different. The story has requirements of plot where this has to happen first in order for that to happen next and so on to its conclusion. The more stereotyped the masturbation fantasy, the more crucial are the steps. Each one is filled with meaning. Part of the meaning is a permissive meaning allowing the next step to occur. Often they are progressive steps in the validation of self-esteem and self-confidence by making the object vulnerable in a certain way that corresponds to the vulnerability of the self. The progressive transformation of the object to vulnerable corresponds in its inverse to the progressive strengthening of the self.

Stereotyped masturbation fantasy has the same structure as a fetish with rigid iconography, fixed sequences. The fixed sequence is necessary in order to reach orgasmic conclusion. This is a fetish structure. Again we see that fetish is a process concept and not a content concept. Men and women with this type of stereotypy in their masturbation fantasy will sometimes embarrassingly say that they enjoy masturbation more than actual sex in reality. While literally true in one sense, it isn't true in another sense. It just makes actual sex a different category of experience. In actual sex is the potential for growth that stereotyped masturbation precludes, if it doesn't develop. Yet for them, actual sex is usually inhibited from expressing the required meaning.

A first step in growth can be a better approximation of the masturbation fantasy in sex, with another in reality. It is a better living out of the fantasy. This can be very frightening at first and ultimately very fulfilling. To achieve this, it of necessity involves another person and a real relationship even though it is a sexual game. But once there are two people involved, even rigidly adhering to the original script, there is the potential for casual, spontaneous new details and therefore for the evolution of the script and for a better emotional synthesis involving growth and development of the self and the relationship.

Example

An outwardly ebullient young man, is very successful in his studies but not in the real world of career. He has many women attracted to the zest of his personality, to his charm and humor, but spurns all those who want him. They are not the ones he wants. They are choosing him. He wants to choose the woman. But with these, he is too anxious to approach. He has a masturbation fantasy in which he is at a bar and sees a woman, alone, at the other end. He struggles to gain the courage to approach her and ends up in bed with her. When I ask for the details, the following emerges. She's an extremely good looking, very well dressed, self-possessed, self-confident, quiet, self-contained, haughty and cold woman, drinking alone at the bar, calmly smoking a cigarette and tossing her head as she exhales. She looks mildly contemptuous. She seems to say, approach me if you dare. No man dares approach her. Instead of feeling his usual hesitancy and self-accusations of cowardice, in his masturbation fantasy he feels coldly empowered. He walks up to the bar and sits down next to her. He ignores her as he calmly orders a drink from the bartender. I'll drink what she is drinking, he says, without acknowledging her in any other way. The bartender pours his drink and our hero says to the woman, without looking at her, what are we drinking. She answers single barrel bourbon. He then reverses the drinks and sips hers. She then tastes his. He has not looked at her since he first saw her across the room. When he tastes her bourbon and when she then tastes his, what began as desire when he looked at her, what became intensity when he heard her speak, responding to his question, intensified when she allowed the exchange of drinks, and then more so when she sipped his. He knew then that the rest was assured; inevitable. There was now no chance of rejection.

They would have sex. For him, they just did. It was all symbolized by her sip of his bourbon. With this step, this reassurance, he can now feel confidant and now he has a full strength erection. Her response, her sip of his bourbon, is the yielding to him that foretells the ultimate conquest. All performance anxiety that he experiences in real life, all low self-esteem anxieties about his appeal and value, are overcome by the strength of the rigid erection he now feels. He knows that if she accepts the exchange of drinks she will accept the exchange of other fluids. It is then, and only then that she calmly says she will go to the bathroom and take off her underpants and when she comes back she will sit on his lap at the bar and they will have sex in public without any of the others knowing. He is to have his orgasm inside her without any facial or verbal display. In the fantasy, her voice is very calm, commanding and totally confident. Her tone excites him to the acceleration phase. Now he can accept the woman wanting him. In the fantasy, she's instantly back and he turns to her and surreptitiously opens his fly for his penis to emerge and she sits on his lap. In the fantasy, he effortlessly enters and his orgasm occurs at that moment.

I ask if the fantasy continues after orgasm and indeed it does. They calmly finish their drinks and as they walk out the door, she tosses her underpants. It seems to be both a gesture of triumph over, and dismissive contempt for, the audience. I ask if she orgasms and he says he doesn't know. He assumes so. It isn't clearly pictured in the fantasy.

I say that it is a story about the ambition to overcome contemptuous rejection. The fear is of contempt of him by her and by himself, ostensibly if he fails but actually a problem for him in everyday life. So it is about his wish to be brave enough to transform his fear of rejection into a yielding by the woman and triumphant admiration. I say he doesn't know if she has an orgasm because she and her orgasm are secondary to the role she plays. It is her participation in the drama of her role function that is the reassurance. Her love and admiration for him is expressed by her being turned on to this drama which is so meaningful and important to him. That it is also meaningful and important to her is the proof that he is meaningful and important to her.

He agrees but he's somewhat unimpressed with this formulation because while it rings true to him, he wants the satisfaction in reality. Otherwise he is a coward. I tell him his cowardice is based on one not two but should be based on two not one. The two is the woman and himself and that he contaminates her by assuming she won't be excited by this sexual game and therefore by him and so it must remain in fantasy. As long as he has to conquer the unwilling and prove himself to the rejecting, he will be anxious but worse, should he prevail in reality she is at that moment no longer useful or wanted by him, because he has conquered and, driven by conquest, he must go on to the next, closing the circle of rejection but this time it is her rejected not him. He is then doomed to compulsively repeat as he does in masturbation. The stereotyped fantasy repetition need is the proof of the unsustainability of the fantasy. He therefore must find his self-esteem in himself.

He now is tearful and says hopeless. I say he feels it is hopeless because he has accepted the reality of another fantasy, one of his worthlessness. I say let us hear that fantasy. I say this is the real work of his analysis.

In noting progress in his treatment, one looks for the fantasy to begin to be elaborated. Perhaps her personality becomes elaborated. Perhaps she puts her hand tenderly on his as he holds her glass after his first sip. And if such a detail were to emerge, would it be a turnoff or a turn on. Hopefully, the touch is imagined as softly tender and hopefully that is exciting. Sometimes the masturbation fantasy appears as a dream and is elaborated there. We are looking for an increased tolerance for risk of a deeper relationship without rejection of him and without aggression against her by humiliation of her value to him.

In therapeutic quest of this progress, we can show that the element of profound acceptance of him above all others begins when she allows him to sit next to her and to order the same drink and to switch glasses, each step exciting. The two glasses with the same drink symbolizes their union in complete idealized identical acceptance of the other. But she is more competent and her posture more phallic, both of which he aspires to. We can show that she needs him to be her affirmative as much as he needs her for his affirmation. If only he will recognize that, he will be brave because he will realize he is giving her what she needs so she can give him what he needs.

If the fantasy were hers rather than his, and if she were a rigidly controlling woman who needed to be seduced into sex, she would then have the conflict. It is an attitude conflict. "Don't tell me what to do!" Except in sex, where it excites her. But she isn't happy about that and refuses to acknowledge it to herself. It is fully revealed in masturbation fantasy. And enacted. Her ideal man is therefore a mosaic! Therapy tries to help her understand that she has a conflict with her power and authority within her and that sex isn't the problem, it's an adaptation attempt at a partial solution. As she becomes more understanding of and comfortable with this conflict, and less ashamed of the sexual fantasy with its yielding hence feared submission hence implied weakness, she can either comfortably accept her mild disassociation or come to a different somewhat more integrated compromise where she is not so dominating in relationships and not so submissive in the sexual fantasy. But she might become more relaxed in relationships and have the same sexual fantasies. For the analyst, these are differences without a distinction. Any more comfortable and adaptive compromise represents an easing of the emotional conflict if therapy can help her with self-esteem to bring a more relaxed attitude to her ego ideal and her relationship to that part of herself and therefore less anxiety.

Masturbation fantasy undergoes evolution. It begins whenever masturbation begins, late latency, early adolescence, or later adolescence, or young adulthood. It accretes and tunes its plot until early adulthood. Then it becomes fixed or more slowly develops. What develops is the plot as revealed by the details, particularly where orgasm occurs. This can reveal the conclusion and therefore the hidden motivation. During growth and development of the life cycle and personality, the fantasy reflects either a healthy result of healthy progression in the life cycle or as consolation for failure or frustration. Often it is both.

The masturbation fantasy that seems like a trial action is actually a trial self. How does it feel to be the wished for self. The fantasy is where everything that happens is under the control of the self. It represents an attempt to adapt not only to the imagined and feared reality but also to the emotional meanings of the new self. The adaptations the self needs to make are to the new self, the vicissitudes of growth and development, as well as of reality. Adaptation is required throughout the life cycle, not just in the phase of physical adolescence but to adulthood, to middle age and to old age. Erikson described these phases and their natural adaptations. Conflicts with the ego ideal often are paramount in neurotic stalemates of growth. Early emotional strain traumas in attachment are particularly relevant in the genesis of stalemates.

The masturbation venue is a creative venue just like the dream function but is often overlooked and its revelatory potential denied because of shame about the act and more so, about the fantasy, details and plot. Creativity is an ego function and the ego function of the patient will organize the content and use of the fantasy.

The more stereotyped it is, the more anxiety is contained, articulated, disguised and brought to its conflicted compromise conclusion. When masturbation fantasy is stereotyped, it is an unconscious fantasy in status nascendi. At the end of the story, it is always the end of the middle of the story. The end is frozen, the story development is frozen, at the end of the beginning or the middle of the middle. Any compulsive aspect is the proof that something is yet to be satisfied and that the road to satisfaction and perhaps satisfaction itself is poisoned by anxieties of conflict.

Masturbation by another is a most interesting variant. Popularized nowadays as a massage with a happy ending, it is ostensibly just a form of sex without sexual disease transmission risk. But it is also an actualization of a masturbation fantasy that now incorporates another person, a real person. As such, it has the opportunity for variation unless rigidly scripted. There is apparently a natural script to it in which the masseuse while massaging the customer, massages closer and closer to the sensitive parts. The masseuse's art is to pick up the cues of where and when, what and how. The customers' part is to assume the role they are comfortable with, from actively scripting to actively enjoying the passivity, depending on their core masturbation fantasy. In this way, aspects of the real relationship between them and sex can be disavowed as just a massage, or even just a massage with a happy ending, but disavowing its relationship to the psychology of the customer. The fantasy can vary from active to passive, from above or below in the dominance hierarchy of economic class or age, from beholden to enslaved, from extralegal to entitled. But it is a fantasy obviously enacted into reality, and there is its usefulness as an illustration in therapy. The sensory emotional details of the enactment will tell the deeper meaning tale.

Mutual masturbation by lovers is the socially acceptable form. It is a conscious wish to please the other and to feel the power to help or make another reach orgasm. It can represent an unconscious wish for the other to accept the self's masturbation fantasy.

Pornography

Pornography can be used alone or with someone – along an enhancement spectrum, from curiosity, to desire aid, arousal aid, to orgasm aid or enhancement – but perhaps is most commonly used as an aid to masturbation. It is a prepackaged, always reliable and never changing dramatized masturbation fantasy. For those whose imagination lacks intense reality qualities, so important for intense sensory-emotional experience, pornography helps provide it. Where there are inhibitions about fully acknowledging and exploring the contents of one's masturbation fantasy, the prepackaged variety seems to place the responsibility for content on the pornographer. If it does get around in inhibition, its advantage is it works, and it tends to always work.

When pornography is linked to masturbation, and is the fantasy to which masturbation coincides, the details and nodal points are as useful to therapy as non-porno masturbation. The idea that it isn't as useful because it is someone else's creation overlooks the vast porno literature available and the free choice the user has to pick that which excites. The plot, the characters, the change in relationship as the scene proceeds, the sensory emotional details of revealed anatomy, are all where the revelations of meaning are. Porno users almost always have a relatively narrow repertoire and some have one favorite watched over and over. There is the location of the story of meaning.

Because it can be chosen to be that which especially turns one on, fetish and fetish enactments are always available and not dependent on finding a partner in reality. Probably it tends to fetishize any sex in the sense that it focuses usually on the body parts of the sex act itself. More elaborated movie types of story with pornography are perhaps less common and perhaps because those capable of enjoying it are less frequent porno customers because they are capable of imagining their own porno stories with greater specificity and therefore more enjoyment.

Pornography has existed for many centuries. Its latest iteration is on the Internet. There, it is dramatic and involves watching real people having sex. It is an industry. It is said that a danger is the disassociation of sex from relationships and bodies in reality. It is also said to risk addiction. But there were many young people who felt addicted to masturbation long before there was Internet availability of pornography.

Another danger is said to be the objectification of women's bodies. Of course, it is. It is also an objectification of men's bodies. It is also an objectivization of the sexual act. It is also an objectification of the relationship. To some extent, actual sex has similar elements. After all, arousal is to the body and hopefully to the person and the experience of the person, but also specifically to the body and parts of the body. So these are the dangers of the person more than the media.

Perhaps its worst danger is the availability of criminal acts, most appallingly, child abuse. The Internet makes it difficult to track and arrest perpetrators. This is the criminal part of the business. It is a forensic issue. The use of children in this way is sadistic. Appalling. The perpetrators seem on the face of it, sociopathic; betrayers of trust. It is a police matter. The vast majority of pornography is not that.

As discussed over and over again, in this book, the story of meaning involves the personality, its yearnings and its fears. Those addicted to pornography often have an inhibition. They don't do what they want to do in reality. Most often it's not because it is criminal but because they have a Madonna versus whore disassociation of sex whereby what they most desire they assume would not excite a good woman. They may not have an available partner. An interesting challenge to this are the recent apps where men or women can dial up a date for sex, an evening's encounter, and even specify what it is they want. Then there is no excuse about no willing partner. The inhibited will not be able to use the app. There is the evidence which therapy can use to change a complaint of unavailability to a clarified symptom of inhibition.

The point is pornography is a masturbation fantasy. The masturbation fantasy is revelatory of meaning even more sometimes than actual sex because the fantasy is always the way one wants it to be. It has more clarity, therefore, as to meaning. And the meaning is the meaning of emotional desire not just of sexual desire. But emotional desire must be liberated from the sexual scene. The patient themselves has to do that in treatment because the meanings of the scenes are their meanings. The therapeutic technique that helps them do this involves the patient associating to the sensory emotional details with special attention to the nodal points that catalyze the next phase of the arousal cycle. Those nodal points usually represent a change in the emotional other.

Masturbation as a Transitional Object

Transitional objects are the use of an object in reality for an emotional experience, midway between fantasy and reality. Masturbation has aspects of this mix in that it is the use of the reality body to enhance fantasy. The link between fantasy and phases of sexual arousal makes this even more powerful. Masturbation is the grandiosity of the possible. It's about the imaginary experience of what really might happen. It could have happened. It might happen. If it's a memory replay, it did happen. And for a few moments, masturbation allows one to really feel in the body the way one wants to really feel about the self.

Masturbation is a story about sex and the sexual object but it's also a story about the self and ideal feelings about the self. The fantasy is about the self, free to experience in an imaginative drama, the scene in which various wishes can be realized and traumas can be overcome, in a way that feels both natural and good. If something needs to be proven about the self, it will be proven there. If there's a conquest to be made, any particular way it must be made, it will be there in the masturbation story. The novelistic scenes of human nature's conundrums are depicted.

For the imaginative, for the strong sensory experiencers, thing presentation imaginary scenes with reality qualities are almost as good as reality in validating the emotional meaning. The exteroceptive sensory system is stimulated as strongly in masturbation as in conjoint sex. The analysis of the masturbation fantasy can investigate the emotional meaning of the sensory details of the imagination scene just as if it were in reality.

A beautiful film about this, taking masturbation to the next stage of fantasy reality mix, is *Lars and the Real Girl*. In the film, Lars, a socially inhibited young man, sends away for an anatomically correct doll and treats her as real. The whole town gets in on the act and slowly helps the story progress until Lars is ready for a live human being. Each step in the drama prepares him for the next step.

It illustrates the potential of masturbation to provide a growth and development pathway for the self with the observing ego playing the part of the townspeople. In the film, masturbation is portrayed as a reparative story. This is probably a universal feature. It is reparative of self-esteem and self-confidence. It reassures us that we will be able to find the partner of our dreams in the ways we need to find them, to use and be used in the ways we need, yet in total control so that it isn't how we fear, indeed, it overcomes what we fear. The fantasy is controllable in every detail whereas actual reality is not, therefore, the plot, hidden in all these details, can succeed in all its elements and therefore in its conclusion. The conclusion is orgasm, but, really, the conclusion is emotional satisfaction.

The ability to have the whole story progress in a growth and development trajectory depends on how neurotic the conflicts and how flexible the ego versus how rigidly defended. Creativity is an ego function and will work automatically, depending on talent, if free to do so. It is an aspect of personal growth and development as a whole.

A masturbation fantasy may not be enacted, but if it is enacted, it is always also a masturbation fantasy. The exception is sometimes an action oriented person, usually a woman, who enacts but claims it is being enacted at her rather than from her, and who claims that she does not have such a masturbation fantasy although she is clearly intensely excited to orgasm by the enactment. Often such a person denies any fantasy during masturbation. To a psychoanalyst, this is a distinction without a difference. Fantasy can be experienced in action only. This is true of the acting out of attitude in object relations for the nonsexual content emotional areas as well. The point is, whether active or passive, action or fantasy, the scenario is intensely exciting and therefore emotionally meaningful, and it is a fantasy in which the person is playing a role. The claim is that it is meaningful only because it is exciting but to the analyst, it is also exciting only because it is meaningful.

Psychic Structures

In the various disclaimers are illustrations of characteristic personality defenses. Disavowal, rationalization, role reversal, avoidance of responsibility, inhibitions of self-ownership, of desire, are all examples. These mechanisms will be found as general personality defenses in nonsexual, interpersonal relationships and attitudes as well because they are characteristic of the person.

Because the masturbation scenes picture the person as they wish to be, aspects of their ego ideal are revealed. This ideal for the self will play an important role in their psychology in general, as an ideal to be lived up to. Pictured will be the ideal way to achieve this ideal state. That may be by conquering, by waiting, by seduction, by ownership, by being owned. There are infinite combinations and variations. These themes and their attitudes and strategies will be repeated in internal and external object relations. The healthier will show this in realistically tempered and modulated derivatives and compromises.

The superego of neurotic moral self-attack is apparent in the self-state at the beginning of the fantasy, if it is forlorn, needy, anxious, or sad. This is the motivation for the next step in the fantasy, the gradual transformation of the self to the wished for self and the ego ideal. All variations are possible. All are revealing of meaning.

The ego's integration capacity is also revealed. Are the characters extreme and renditions of opposite, un-integratable affect states, or are they more modulated integrations? Does the story show an evolution of variations of conflict toward a greater synthesized conclusion or is each element separate and at the conclusion still separate albeit more satisfactory in relationship to each other?

Each self-state and character may be playing a psychic structure agency role and the plot is about the relationship of conflict in the self. The fantasy's orgastic conclusion is a temporary resolution. The reality qualities of the sensory physical experience, helping in validating the emotional meaning, suddenly with orgasm are doing the reverse by seeming to claim the satisfaction is and must be in reality only. Thus is the reality conundrum still fixed and the repetition compulsion energized for a repeat frustration in reality and a repeat masturbation fantasy without change.

For any change to occur, there must be inner change in the person themselves. The compromise of forces must ease up on the stalemate and begin to elaborate, grow and develop, so that the narrative moves along. They are always afraid that the excitement will be lost if they do. This is a retribution fantasy that's part of what they are seeking to compromise. It represents guilt and shame over the fantasy and over their desires. If the change is coming naturally through life or through therapy, then the details to which the excitement is placed will change, or the details will be the same but meaning will be different, more complicated, because what is exciting in the fantasy is developing. But the excitement is not lost unless they have attacked it themselves.

Sometimes with growth the fantasy becomes more primitive, more undisguised, and therefore temporarily more distressing to the patient. But this again, is an attack. Less of a disguise means more available to understand the concepts involved and to be able to put them into concepts and words and for the patient therefore to understand themselves better. As the fantasy becomes more primitive, their object relationships in life tend to become calmer and more maturely integrated. What they seek in reality tends to become more realistic, and more satisfied. The therapist plays a crucial role in relationship to the patient if this change is occurring. Interpreting the effect of the change and showing how any self-attack is occurring because of the change, is an important part of catalyzing the growth that is occurring. Interpreting the effect of an interpretation is a standard and necessary part of psychoanalytic work and necessary for many patient's ego growth. It is easy then to interpret the need for that second interpretation because of a self-attack by the patient.

Chapter 7

Threesomes

Threesomes are not uncommon in couples. It is either enacted in reality, in conscious fantasy, only during times of stress, or during sex, or always unconsciously. The third is often a real person, past or present. It functions differently for different people and different couples. It serves an emotional function. Ostensibly about sexual excitement, it is more deeply about the vicissitudes of attachment. The third is a magnet and a container, an evocator and an intensifier: for excitement, for anxiety, for sadness, for mourning, for idealization, for constancy, for hope, for central emotional needs.

Needs are not satisfied in a couple because of limitations in the couple. The relationship may be further depriving when one individual needs the third because of conflict about their own needs. Their inner conflict causes them to externalize their need from themselves to the other and to the other relationship.

When the limit is because of one in the couple, for instance rigid and angry, there is a deprivation for the other one in the couple. These deprivations may awaken a fantasy of a third or an acting out of that fantasy with a real third. This is a particular danger when the deprived one is either too inhibited to confront their partner or their partner is too angry or ill to be able to respond to confrontation. Then the third is an alternate pathway for a more sustaining attachment.

But the third may be necessary for reasons of inability to attach securely or to be assertive enough to help build a healthy relationship. Then the third is used to sooth and to supplement. The more it actually does that, the more it delays the resolution of the mental conflict.

Threesomes in human sexual fantasy and in lived experience is a common theme. It is commonly enacted. This is because in human development, there is a growth in childhood from twosomes to threesomes. The threesome in the beginning is not yet solid. It tends to be experienced as a twosome within a threesome, that is, two twosomes. Who is number one and who is number two, who is in and who is out, at any point in time, is very important to the child. Mirror mirror on the wall, who is the fairest of them

DOI: 10.4324/9780429491733-8

all! And as grandparents are fond of saying, to each grandchild, "I love you the best. Don't tell the others."

Envious competition and aggression are ubiquitous. The pain of being left out or feeling less than is motivating. Add to this the problems of aggressive dissociations in love and sex, the envy and competitive aggression and self-esteem problems in some personality disorders, and you get compensatory threesomes in fantasy or reality being a common neurotic adaptation. The therapy issue isn't having more than one. The issue is why the more than one is needed. The issue isn't who is number one. The issue is whether or not there is a number one; a one relationship with an integrated experience of the main partner as an companionate, sexual and romantic relationship. The further therapy issue is why isn't the one relationship feeling good enough?

Any adult who has trouble within themselves with that number one feeling, that is both special and not grandiose, may be tempted to the threesome idea. Anyone with certain attachment insecurities who needs the insurance plan of an available other is susceptible to the threesome idea. Anyone who splits their sexual life between the intimate one and the sexual one is attracted to the threesome. Anyone with trouble with commitment may have a present one now and a remembered past one, denigrated then but idealized now, yearned for again now in fantasy and in memory, against whom the present one is compared unfavorably, and is used to prevent a commitment feeling to the regular partner.

Anyone with a special sexual need, fetish and fetish enactments, who experiences shame or partner refusals, is ripe for a threesome. When there is a special sexual act, or fetish or fetish enactment that contains the idealization and cannot be satisfied in reality or fantasy with the commitment partner, a disassociation motivation may recruit an extra marital lover who is excited by or at least acquiesces. Then the special idealization from possession of the fetish is experienced and the self-esteem bolstered.

We are not talking about a threesome that is just fine with all three. We are not talking about the privations of separation by circumstance: war, migration, school, illness or business. There are as many motivations and mixtures as there are threesomes. But psychologically these are defined as threesomes of circumstance. Their psychological significance is usually as another twosome, in addition to the primary twosome.

One of the most common types of threesomes is the married person with a fantasy or a remembered ideal of an actual lover. The split is not an all good or bad separation between the two, but rather two ambivalently held objects. The most common is the stable and unexciting life partner and the exciting lover. If there is sex with the stable partner, it is described as ordinary or boring. The sex with the lover is described as intensely exciting. Intensely exciting sex is clearly expressing a longed-for idealization of the self, never or no longer satisfied by the marital relationship. The failure to have married the sexually exciting one is often for the unconscious fear of the power it gives the other over the emotional life of the self. If the marriage splits up and the lover is married, there are either many angry storms ahead or the sexual excitement settles down as the relationship comes into reality and normal ambivalence ensues and now has to be contained and overcome within the confines of one committed relationship.

Rarely, there is the situation of marriage to the exciting sexual partner and the extramarital affair is with a better intimacy object, someone more capable of an emotional relationship in-depth with thoughtful concern. The problem here is that the sexual life is with the disturbed relationship. But when the intimate relationship is with a good friend, we label that normal.

Example

A patient receives an emergency phone call that his grandfather has just passed away after presenting to the emergency room with chest pain. The call is from a woman he has never heard of before. At the emergency room, he meets a woman, his grandfather's age, who tells the story of their relationship. The grandfather, fleeing oppression, left his wife and two young children to come to America, to establish himself and bring them to him. On a long journey through Europe, he stopped in a small town and was welcomed to a warm meal by a woman he stopped to talk to while switching trains at the local train station. He tarried with her longer than he planned and an intense love affair developed causing her to go with him to America where he placed her in a separate home. Then, as planned and promised, he brought his wife and children over. Every Wednesday for the next 60 years, he spent the day with his lover. She never married, never wanted to have children, so it was perfect for her. She lived a family life vicariously through his, the continuing saga of which she eagerly listened to at each visit. Each time she would give him some advice about family relationships in his marriage and child rearing, usually counseling loving patience and limit setting rather than punishment. So she knew the son who she called and had his name and number as next of kin although he had never met her. By the time he did, his mother had already passed. He has said nothing to his family. He kindly invited her to the funeral. She came, introduced as a business friend of the grandfather's. She cried when she met her lover's grown children and their children. They thought she was crying over the loss of her friend. She was crying at finally meeting the family she loved in the only way she could. She never expected to have that sweet pleasure. There has been no further contact. Perhaps there need not be, a certain satisfaction already having been achieved. But it's probably guilt that requires the alienation. Unclear in the story is whether the lover was primarily for sex or for companionship or perhaps for both. But its duration argues in favor of companionship as a major factor.

Example

A man and a woman each have separate, stable, happy marriages. They have each other as their extramarital lover. It is described as a purely sexual relationship and they meet about once a month. Their sexual relationship includes what they call "kinky" sexual enactments that each is ashamed to bring into their marriage. Perhaps more importantly, they have married partners who wouldn't be turned on by such things. What neither is aware of is their very different personalities. The sexual partners are very intense. The marital partners are very calm. The sexual partners' sexuality is very intense. The marital partners' sexuality is not. Because of the intensity of the lover's personalities, they avoid disagreeing at all costs, each sensing that a fight could easily alienate. And so they keep the relationship at a distance, geographically and temporarily. Their meetings are titrated by the intensity of their mutual need, they think for sex, but perhaps for romantic specialness at the cutting edge of idealization.

Example

A married couple takes a date night once a month because sexual abandon, a feeling of freedom, is hard to achieve in a family with young children. They have a babysitter, and they go to a local hotel. Sometimes, they each arrive separately. Then, they may meet at the bar, pretending to be strangers. They enact a first date scenario that, of course, ends up in bed. The courtship of the evening varies according to the sexual fantasies of each. The bedroom encounters may be just the same as usual or may involve some variation. But there is also variation of dress, where each surprises each. For instance, once he arrived in his old army uniform, which she had never seen. For a moment, a delicious moment for them both, she didn't recognize him. In this way, they incorporate the fantasy third into their actual relationship. The third is the fantasy of the stranger met spontaneously at a bar. Anything could happen. There are exciting unknown possibilities. This allows for the emotional dissociation of the romantic sexual ideal from dilution by the mundane and the ambivalent daily real relationship yet preserves the exclusivity of the marital relationship.

Example

Another couple achieves the same goal through circumstance. She is an upper level businesswoman, very successful, and travels worldwide on business and is away a third of the year. They talk nightly while she's away. The reunions are intense for both of them, intense both emotionally and sexually. Was it May West who said about such arrangements, "keeps the dew on the rose." Here is the marital partner as the newly experienced third. Here again, the couple is functioning as its own third.

Example

An older adult man has an intensely sexual marriage with a stormy woman he must please and you would think if he had a lover, it would be for tea and sympathy. Instead, once every few weeks, he goes to a sex worker. He always chooses a young woman who looks innocent but is very skilled, at listening! His fantasy is of being emotionally serviced rather than of having to do service. His fantasy is she is only skilled with him because she looks up to him and wants to please him so much. His fantasy is of her soft, interested emotional receptivity, against his wife's hard personality. He is soft with her. He mostly talks and she mostly listens. It may end with sex or it may not on any given occasion. As with all sex work patrons, he goes not because it's easy in but because it's easy out. She is therefore a safe third. She will be no threat to the marriage as long as their arrangement is secret. He pays her with cash. With his wife, he services her and there is no out! And she has his credit card, not a limited and controllable aliquot of cash.

Example

A mild-mannered man has a relationship with a calm woman and they raise a family with love for the children and for the mission of parenting but with growing stalemate in their own emotional relationship. Sex between them is never hot and gradually disappears. The man has a sexual fantasy of domination and submission he begins to act out with a younger woman at work. He takes her out to dinner where she starts a fight and they return to her apartment where he administers a spanking. He prefers her lying on his lap and she prefers bending over the bed. It's the only true disagreement they have! They then have intercourse and he leaves. He is intensely ashamed and fears discovery and so it took him several years to talk about it even with his own therapist. He couldn't imagine doing that with his own wife, both because she never fights with him and because the act itself he feels is a despicable domination. Here is the example of a third needed for a dissociated special sexual event. Sex with his wife has disappeared. With the lover, he will have sex and a phallic feeling. Here he will be the boss.

Example

Two people are in a marriage that is intensely sexual including mutual fetish enactments. But neither understands the other emotionally nor is it possible for them to calmly engage in intimate emotional interaction. Each of them has a different nonsexual friend who they talk with once a week about the problems in their marriage, the raising of children, their work, their families of origin and other topics of concern. Neither marital partner considers themselves to be having an affair. Each of the stormy marital partners is glad for the friendship relationship the other has because it relieves some of the burden and consequences of their stormy marriage. This is exactly the same third equilibrium as in the previous example but often overlooked because the third is not the sexual part of the triangle. Sometimes a therapist plays that role.

There are many examples of the unavailable one who formed the constant threesome in the thoughts and fantasies of one member of a couple. These are the fantasy love affairs with many variations. There is the one who got away. There is the one who was never asked but should have been. There is the one who was mistakenly rejected. There is the one who couldn't be because of structural barriers; their marriage, their dwelling in a distant country, because they came on the scene after the marriage, because they're from a different generation. Exactly the same but with a future orientation is the one who has yet to be found, again for various reasons. In all cases, there is longing and idealization of the lost one or the sought one, or the impossible one or the almost one. All so near yet so far, so far yet so dear. If there is a steady relationship or marriage, there is loneliness and denigration and disavowal of the importance of the present relationship and reluctance to confront the present relationship problems.

The secret emotional hiding places of thirds can go on for many years. It reflects the stalemated natural growth of the present relationship whereby reality tempers idealization and ambivalence enters without the capacity to build tolerance and resiliency. The lonely forlorn and disassociated what if and only if fantasies are all defenses against the deepening growth of a relationship in present time. Patients like this are afraid to go all in but cannot be alone and go all out. They split their comfort object and their romantic ideal object into two separate objects. The reasons within them that their previous relationships haven't worked are for the same reasons that the present one is unsatisfactory. It is also the reason that if Miss or Mr. Right of the future should magically appear now, the old hesitancy and ambivalence pattern would assert itself.

The issues in all the stories are twofold. The first is the problem within the main relationship and the second is the dissociation. What is the problem in the main relationship and what is dissociated varies and perhaps infinitely so. Dissociation can involve any conflict and emotional paradigm. We are used to seeing it perhaps more obviously in the disassociation of sexual behavior but it occurs in emotional experience as well.

Clearly, there is a spectrum. There is a saying that the most beautiful woman in the world can give you no more than what she has. The correct statement would be that it is a rare relationship that gives anyone, man or woman, everything one needs and wants. This is not a psychoanalytic treatment problem. It is a counseling problem about adaptation to reality. The psychoanalytic problem is for people who cannot integrate satisfying sex in a satisfying emotional relationship. The psychoanalytic problem is not circumstance, bad luck, nor different growth within a couple. The problem is when a person cannot and never has been able to integrate their own emotional and sexual life such that their sexual object, their intimate object, their commitment object and their romantic object are integrated in mind in a good enough compromise with life and with themselves. The psychoanalytic problem emerges when such people are unhappy and unsatisfied. The capacity to integrate components of love relationships means stronger resilience in the face of reality deprivations and a better tolerance of reality dissatisfactions, without a fall in self-esteem. What is needed is integration of ambivalence, of positive and negative thoughts and feelings, of love and anger, both within a stable relationship to a love object. These emotional challenges do not come out of nowhere. They come not only from the human emotional condition. They come from the attachment problems and traumas of developing human beings as well as from their emotional reactivity.

Attachment problems and traumas always affect self-esteem. The child feels unimportant and unworthy when a parent does not make attachment, a forever positive regard and commitment, the most precious aspect of their relationship with their child. Attachment problems evoke strong emotional reactions of fight and flight. Emotional reactions are mixed and very intense. It is their intensity and not just the mixture, that makes it difficult to integrate them. Because attachment traumas occur in reality, their defenses, their sufferings, dissociations, repressions and neurotic compromises of course include the sexual function, a mixture of reality and fantasy for all human beings. Sexual traumas within the family are dramatic not only because of what happens physically but the damage done to attachment of secure bonding. That it happened at all is often a reflection of insecure attachment in the family of which the sexual trauma is only the acute manifestation. The chronic low-grade emotional strain trauma aspect is perhaps even more debilitating. As a colleague said, someone spit in the love soup.

For each patient, the mixture of inborn intensity problems, of autonomous ego endowments, reality trauma, ego illnesses, of the real security of emotional attachment, all vary. It is what makes psychological work with human beings so infinitely interesting. All these aspects are seen clearly in sexual behavior and fantasy.

The cruel irony of neurosis and insecure attachment is that it tends to repeat itself. This is because the damage done is within the person and no longer just within relationships. But it seems to the person as if the problem is in relationships and the particular partners chosen. The third is an attempt at a solution without having to give up the ambivalently held attachment to the marital partner, because the strength of the ambivalence correlates with the strength of the attachment! This is because ambivalence becomes a defense against attachment. Secure attachment seems an impossibility and attachment reawaken history and trauma history of insecure attachment. This must be defended against in one of the best ways to do it is to use ambivalence to prevent secure attachment that would seem like a prison where repetition of insecurity seems probable. Thus is brought about what is feared. This cruel repetition in relationship to the self is what Freud referred to as the repetition compulsion. Locked into the familiar suffering, attached to reassuring familiarity, but wounded by its deprivation trauma and determined to master it, the patient unwittingly seeks over and over again to escape, only to repeat. Dante's Purgatorio where that which we are is our own version of hell. Very sad.

When such patients come for treatment, they rarely come because they have seen their own problem. They come for advice about relationships and finding the right one. The opportunity arises when, inevitably, if allowed, the patient feels the same ambivalence to the therapist and has the feeling that the therapist isn't the ideal or even the right one. Now comes the opportunity to analyze in detail and in real time these attachment issues with the patient.

Treatment

Treatment involves understanding the meaning of the repetitions of the third. The transference is used as a real-time example of the same dynamics that interfere with all of their intimate relationships. Now can come an exploration of the meaning of this experience for them, usually free of the compelling and consuming sexual disguise. The attachment insecurity, the danger signals that any attachments revive, the fantasy dangers they conjure, the defensive emotional retreat the fantasy danger stirs, can all be more clearly understood. Sometimes at a certain point in the exploration and clarification of these problems, the patient may have romantic idealization fantasies about the therapist. This offers a similar opportunity to understand these phenomena, now from the point of view of idealization rather than denigration but with exactly the same story with exactly the same dynamics.

In the fantasy, the perfect one living happily ever after is the hidden story of the wished for infinitely stable, un-ambivalent emotional attachment. In the denigrated present partner, is the story of the fear of commitment to a less than perfect object because of the fear of the lack of stability in an emotional relationship in the face of reality ambivalence. Hidden in both sides of the story are the traumatic attachment memories of the patient and the need for an un-ambivalent relationship that is not only impossible in reality but would be boring if it were possible. Perhaps Adam and Eve left the Garden for Edan for a reason other than disobedience, namely, boredom?

Treatment can help by first stabilizing the threesome and calming the agitation about it. This enables a calmer understanding of the meanings of it. Once the situation is seen as emotionally meaningful and not just cruel reality fate, the patient can begin to see the various aspects of their feelings that are separated with each trying to be appeased rather than compromised. These patients don't compromise easily and have a great fear that putting any two together, any two strong feelings, will ruin it all. It also allows the emergence of the real object, a reflection externally of the object internally. That can calm the idealization enough to see what is really missing and what is really there. This clarification of reality, from which they are defended, can help with practical decision making.

One such patient had a childhood memory that after a sibling was born, he could not tolerate two different food groups on the dinner plate touching each other. The juices of the one would ruin the flavor of the other. The two ruining each other was not only the fact of the second sibling but of the highly ambivalent feelings about it. Some people play that out with relationships rather than food. But relationships are nourishment to the soul even as food is nourishment to the body. But if two are to be avoided, perhaps a third will even things out.

The needy, feared, desperate, avoidant, angry, passive attachment style, whatever it is, plays itself out as clearly in the relationship with the therapist as it does in the rest of their lives. One can see its expression in the small things like appointments and payment as well as in the larger emotional displays in the transference.

The most obvious is the patient who arrives already having a therapist but needs another at the same time. They ask either ostensibly for a consultation that goes on and on or for two therapists at the same time. The problem with the one may be the problem of some growing difference in the one with some frightening aspect like aging. Then the second is picked either because no ambivalence has yet had a chance to form or because the new therapist is simply younger. Almost always, the original therapist has not been told about the existence of the second. This makes a mistress of the second and a wife of the first.

Such diversionary arrangements of attachment give the perpetrator the feeling of control and dominance over their own fate. Of course, as the two attachments proceed, and attachment to each deepens, they find that now instead of having one attachment ambivalence, they have two. Instead of one insecurity, they have two. What was to be avoided is in fact actualized. What cannot be handled in emotional experience tends to be handled in reality experience but is then still impossible to resolve.

It is for this reason that the treatment of threesomes cannot be handled by therapeutic dictum. If they could do it better, they would and they wouldn't need therapy. Telling them to drop the one for the other is futile. Even General Douglas MacArthur is reported to have said, never give an order the troops will disobey. Any command in affairs of the heart is also not only futile but naïve, because it fails to understand the necessity of both legs of the triangle. And so it is left for the therapist to discuss the situation and not micromanage it. The purpose of the discussion is to understand the meaning of each, the need each fulfills, the need fear dilemma involved in both, the inability of the patient to put the two together in one relationship, and the personality resistances to the compromises with life that are necessary for full satisfaction.

Often, the divided need is fulfilled physically. If sex is split off, the sexual experience and physicality are often intensely sensually experienced. This fulfills the emotional need because of the meaning to the self of the intense sexual experience. The arousal levels of the other's body, the subjective sensual sensations of experience of it, are highly valued as unique and special. They are often experienced in the tactile modality of touch, in the fingers, tongue, whole body and genital. These are the hug receptors. Possession can be felt in the visual and auditory sensory areas. I am the ruler of all I can see. If tenderness is split off, those features may also be experienced sensually, only sensually or most intensely. Where there is a broader capacity for relationship experience, special belonging may be experienced also in the warmth of familiarity, and the tenderness of embrace, in the visual of the receptive smile, in the smell of the embracing body.

Defenses against the pain and anxiety of insecure attachment can be by dissociations of components of attachment, addictive dependency, or both. The problem with the dissociation of attachment figures into two dependency objects is the return of the addictive dependency on one or both of the split off objects. Meant to diminish the intensity of attachment, the end result is an increased dependency of attachment precisely because neither of the disassociated figures in the third has the entirety of dependency satisfaction nor the safety of reliability. Then, instead of being insecurely attached to one, there is insecure attachment to two.

The felt experience of intense attachment to the sensory details of the dependency object is an example of the shift to concrete reality as symbol that occurs when attachment to the emotional relationship is either impossible or doubted. The subject may worry about the constancy of the object or the constancy of the object may be in doubt because of the unreliability of the object or because of the ambivalence of the subject projecting it onto the object. The body may seem more reliable and unchangeable, stable and reassuring, than the emotional relationship to the person. The sense of safety is a feeling of relaxation and security that comes with proximity to and felt possession of those sensuous parts of the love object. There is felt the unique specialness of the love object to the self.

The intensity of attraction to the physical details of the sexual object is powered by the intense attachment needs of the self. There the unique specialness is felt, but as a property of the object's physicality. There is longing in absences is for proximity to those physical sensuous details.

Treatment can be extremely helpful in reducing destructive projections and helping the patient locate the insecure attachment within themselves, whether or not there is poor object choice and enactment of insecure relationships. Once the anxious ambivalence about attachment is located in the patient, they can explore its origins and seek a greater comfort in their relationships despite ambivalence and to make better choices about reliable objects, then allowing them to remain reliable by not provoking anger and withdrawal in the object or themselves.

A common reason for asking for treatment is when the threesome becomes unstable; the lover wants marriage, or the marital partner unexpectedly discovers there is a lover. Discovery of the lover is notoriously common because of a careless error caused by unconscious guilt or aggression.

Example

A middle-age married man called in a panic because his tempestuous lover was agitating for him to leave his wife and children and marry her. She was now threatening to call his wife. In treatment, he quickly understood that hers was the classic lover's gamble, and his only countermove was to tell his wife! His panic was that his wife would leave him. But in hearing about the relationship, it seemed they had a warm friendship of many years. Although his infantile, narcissistic self-centered demands clearly turned her off, and taxed her patience, she also admired his assertion in career and his success. They were both devoted to family. Encouraged to tell his wife with empathy and concern for her feelings about this situation, and being sure to express his wish to rededicate himself to his marriage, he did tell her, finding to his surprise that she had long suspected this. They both agreed to couples therapy. It turned out that their marriage was sexually hot at first but children and their competition for her attention had driven him elsewhere. Rather than join his wife as a devoted parent and share in that mission thereby to also have some attention and sense of working together, he had fled into the arms of a lover. His lover, single and without children, was someone with whom he wouldn't have to compete for attention. But then, she wanted marriage and children, especially as she was getting older. Couples therapy helped him and his wife rekindle their marriage and find a sex life once again. More importantly, they were able to understand their deep friendship and their deep commitment to the marriage and to their family, and their deep commitment love for each other. Now, with two children reaching young adulthood and freeing them to have more time together, opportunities were there for them to rediscover their love for each other. Individual therapy helped him understand and modulate his narcissistic defenses against feelings of rejection and to enjoy being part of rather than the sole focus.

Of course, in any treatment relationship, the insecure and ambivalent attachment paradigms will be played out in relationship to the therapist. The danger is the breaking off of treatment. The hope is that seen up close by the therapist, the problem can be recognized, described, explored for its deeper and original meanings, and thereby controlled and overcome by the patient. But it can be very difficult to see the fear when it is hidden behind aggression, and the need when it is hidden by withdrawal. The experienced therapist will not be deterred and will understand that in the crisis there is opportunity. These patients need time and patience and the steadiness of the therapist often over a number of years to trust in the reliability of the therapist, to thereby ease anxiety enough to look at the relationship with the therapist and their relationship with significant others throughout their lives. It is always interesting to see which real relationships will be able to tolerate growth and development and which will not.

Patients who have been able to integrate their love objects find a deeper satisfaction in both the relationship and their sexual attachments because the two can now help each deepen. The intensity of excitement in thing presentation physical sensory attachments need not only be driven by anxiety. Without anxiety, the excitement and the deeper relationship can be more satisfying even as it becomes less driven and compulsive. The physicality remains exciting even without the sole focus and compulsiveness.

Chapter 8

BDSM

BDSM is the current term for bondage, domination and sadomasochism. To put them together is perhaps to misunderstand them. Although they are on a spectrum, their motivations and actions can be quite different, whether in fantasy or behavior. Although control of the other is often common to all of them, the difference of dominating control for safety is very different from dominating control to injure, physically or emotionally.

At extremes of violence, it is often exciting to the perpetrator but not necessarily sexually exciting. The violence and sex may be sequential with sex an excuse or rationale for the violence. The key is whether during the violence they are sexually excited. Clearly, regardless, there is a spectrum of aggression, of love, of ego function and of preservation or contamination of the object in reality.

Why is a chapter on this needed in this book? Are fetish and fetish enactments usually with a BDSM theme? Probably not. But the violent ones are notorious and perhaps contaminate the view of all the rest. At the neurotic level, controlling motivations are ubiquitous but can stimulate guilty self-accusations. They may be false accusations based on misunderstood manifest content and neurotic guilt. The neurotic accusation is of violence when the motive may be control of love, not venting of aggression, especially when there is no overt aggression.

Domination-Submission

The dominator's claim is ownership. The submissive's plea is belonging. Abandonment is the fear in both. Special belonging and special validation are needed by them to feel securely held in the attachment bond. The dominator's control proves the ownership over and over. The submissive's yielding proves their belonging, over and over.

DOI: 10.4324/9780429491733-9

Example

A 32-year-old woman likes bondage. She especially likes it when her boy-friend ties her wrists loosely together, so loosely that she could easily get out but tight enough for her to feel, as she says, "secure." She has a sensuous experience of the material but especially of the tightness when she gently pulls her wrists and feels the soft band tighten and strongly limit the extent of the separation of her wrists. She does so gently, so as to tighten the knots only enough to feel the resistance to complete separation. It is that balance she experiences in the physical sensation of the loosely bound but tight con-nection, a particular feeling of the soft but firm knot on her wrists, that she finds so arousing; to be securely held but not constrained, attached but not smothered. Her interpersonal behavior with her boyfriend is similar in that she alternates between close connection and abruptly scheduled busi-ness trips, yet she calls while away, briefly, but a number of times per day, as if testing the limits of separation. After sex, she inevitably gets up and leaves the room and sometimes even the apartment. She likes her boyfriend's monogamy even though she can, on occasional business trips, enjoy a liaison. She is tied yet free. He is free yet tied.

Domination-submission scenarios usually require more than just a physical representation of the attachment bond. They usually also require a demon-stration of an attachment attitude. The attitude needs to be one of yielding to and acceptance of the dominator by the submissive. The attitude of the dominator is command and control of ownership.

The moment of yielding in the fantasy may differ, with different markers of submission, but is usually fixed in the individual fantasy and in the enact-ment of the fetish action. The point of this description is not to prescribe or predict the linkages in the arousal cycle but merely to illustrate the concept of linkage with some specific examples. One representation of yielding may be sexual intercourse. Which orifice is preferred varies. The chosen orifice is special.

The management of aggression within an attachment bond and the ten-derness that needs to be released and the conditions under which that is possible is balanced in the domination submission fetish action. To be domi-nated means to be owned, means to be wanted, means to be cared for, means to be protected. This is a certain type of attachment paradigm.

There is a mixture of punishment versus yielding/submission. Any required apology and forgiveness is a further strengthening of attachment. The punishment may be revenge for hurt pride, to change an attachment to respect, rather than humiliation; a reversal. This is an example of the infinity of complex motives from individual to individual that no diagnostic category can capture nor should ever constrain.

The prelude is important and may involve either seduction and persuasion or firmly ordering. The post orgasmic relationship is similarly important and may involve the change to tender mutuality and appreciation, if not blocked by shame and if the motivation was a defense against love rather than only the expression of controlling aggression.

Yielding, submission, supplication, resignation, are all markers on a continuum. Yielding implies conscious acceptance. Submission involves conscious, voluntary giving in of one's own will to the will of another and to the excitement of another's arousal, which is arousing to the self. On the continuum of domination and submission, the mild form is about control and humbling, not humiliating nor hurting; it is about yielding, not submitting.

Seduction seduces/forces the sub to excitement that is seen by the dom as being withheld by the sub; an excitement that is exciting, even irresistible to the sub; a domination and dominator that is irresistible to the sub. Both feel specially chosen, specially valued. Ultimately, it's about possession, special possession and the rights and obligations that come with that. Special positions or orifices may reflect special ownership possessions and special yielding to love. In fetish and fetish enactments, the specialness is displaced to the thing or the action and only secondarily then to the person.

For some, the dominant meaning is punishment and a sense of guilt may lead them into it. As one said, "the punishment I get is less than the punishment I think I deserve." The conscious punishment deserved may be about aggression or denigration or withholding or teasing, or sex, but the unconscious guilt may be rather a self-blame for the feeling of not being good enough to be and have been lovable as is. But they sexualize the punishment, which then has a primary, conscious, lustful motive. It becomes an exciting conscious masturbation fantasy and enactment.

The book *Fifty Shades of Grey* depicts spanking, and the spanking instrument, with restraints, and a day later, the evolving relationship. It is written by a woman and read by women. Here, there is a clear depiction of spanking and the spanking relationship. There is a sequential reversal of who is dominant and who is submissive before and after the spanking. Most interestingly, it follows this relationship over time where there is a gradual reversal in the whole relationship and the dominant male spanker becomes the yielding supplicant in the relationship. He is now supplicant to the woman who was submissive to the spanking but now is dominant in the relationship. The yielding/submission paradigm is the marker of submission to a devoted and committed strength of attachment; to and with a pseudo forceful but latently pleading dominator.

There is often a history of dominating control by a parent, with varying degrees of anxiety, versus aggression versus parasitism. The variables have to do with the parental variables of aggression: recruitment by seduction versus recruitment by intimidation, child as helper versus slave, anxiety versus aggression, treasured versus denigrated, masochistic versus narcissistic. Spanking in childhood could be only once or could be just a threat but it gives an image for representing the domineering and controlling attachment bond. It then represents the forced domination and submission emotional relations in the real relationship. This may be wished or feared or both in either the dominator, the submissive, or usually both, when the paradigm becomes sexualized. The domination-submission scene can take many different forms.

Example

A highly successful businesswoman has a fetish and fetish enactment with her lover. The crucial scene is after she has seduced him into the seated position with his suit and tie on but his pants down; not just fly open, pants down. His very erect penis is in her mouth. He is helpless to even sit straight as she tongue bathes the head of the penis, bringing him to the point of plateau and then backing off, and then continuing, so that she is in control of his arousal sequence. At some point, when she feels not his impatience but his complete resignation, she brings him slowly to his orgasm.

Her own excitement has built from the seduction to the oral capture. The feel of the erect penis in her mouth, the firmness of the erection and, especially, a certain throbbing motion raise her excitement to its plateau. When she tastes the pre-orgasmic leak, she is almost orgastic and when he ejaculates her orgasm may begin in full strength. It is the only way she is orgastic with him.

Her associations to his ejaculation are to his yielding to her. Her associations to his semen are to his special male essence, given/taken as a benediction of his submission to her. The taste for her is bittersweet, the displacement of her ambivalence onto sensory detail. His orgasm is the most stimulating experience because of the spurting meaning for her, an involuntary shuddering which begins the fall, the detumescence. She laughs and says if there is a soul, surely it is liquid. When she has this in her body, she feels a warmth and peace and complete satisfaction. She feels this in her genital and she sometimes orgasms. She has this essence of him truly and has truly taken it from him and conquered him. She has left him spent and collapsed.

Her associations to the fetish erection firmness are to his personality firmness and its ramrod quality. She finds the penis both hard and soft; hard for his fierce aggression/assertion. Perhaps she thinks he is a real dick head, a comment on his personality. But when she has his dick in her mouth, then he is helpless. Then she feels in control. Then he is the desperate one. Then he will ultimately give up control to her, ejaculate and get soft. The soft penis represents for her a core gentleness in his personality that only she can access. She finds the soft inviting but contemptible. Yes, she gets desperate every few weeks but not for him. It is only for sex. Specifically, it is his erect penis and ejaculation/semen she craves. But the meaning seems to be the conquest she craves.

An association is to one of her favorite movies, the Fassbinder version of the vampire legend, *Nosferatu the Vampire*. She says the movie is about love not death. The vampire falls in love. This is why she is able to detain him until dawn when he dies; he, not her. Her orgasm would be a submission to him and the death of a valued part of herself, a strong defiant part in relationship to strong authority, and so she reverses this with him.

She then wants to be rid of him; as soon as she can. So she only makes love to him at his house. That way she can leave whenever she wants. He has somehow understood this and tries to save oral sex for the second intercourse of the night, perhaps thus to detain her, as if for him, she is the vampire.

It seems as though her post copulum carnelum is an experience of contempt. She seems then to unconsciously experience him as diminished and undesirable. This is preconscious in her object representation and unconscious in her self-representation.

From her associations and context, her fetish and fetish action has a latent story. She is excited by the dominant phallic narcissistic personality she hates and which the exciting penis fetish represents. The sexual enactment allows her to play out her love and her rage without feeling dominated, humiliated or trapped. She seduces and deflates her oppressor. When she gets his pants down and the uniform of the adult becomes the uniform of a boy, a transition point is revealed when she sees his erect penis and then takes it in her mouth. The other transition point is the ejaculation transition moment when the dominator firmness becomes the vanquished softness and the vulnerable becomes the victorious dominatrix. She changes the enraging hard man into the contemptible soft boy and thereby her anger into tenderness. This game releases her excitement. She starts in the submissive position kneeling at his feet but changes this via the sexual enactment so she becomes the dominatrix and he the submissive.

The more he loves their sex, the more enslaved he becomes to it, the more power she has. She may push the envelope to accomplish it. These reversals for both are the point of the enactment.

Thus we see a manifest sexual story and another, nonsexual latent story represented by anatomy and sexual actions and revealed by her associations. As treatment progresses, other latent stories will emerge.

Inherent in the female's dom/sub fantasy with the man as the aggressor may be the denial of responsibility not just for sex but for aggression/assertion and its sexual excitement. Intercourse is an obvious physical metaphor for domination-submission because it can be used to illustrate a fantasy about relationships. Man on top. Woman on bottom. Man inserting. Woman receiving. Is it about love or is it about aggression? Forceful thrusting may illustrate frightening but erotic fantasies of overpowering and joining together in the force of lust. But then the dilemma of how to feel in control and who is in control and what control the receptive partner has, and if there is not complete control, will there be a feeling of anxiety, fear or humiliation. The anxiety is easily eroticized because the anxiety is about the lust. It is lust that feels out of control. It is the anxiety about the drive force of lust and how to control the yielding to one's own lust and to another's lust and associated fantasies.

It helps if someone has basic self-confidence that they can use the lust force for their purposes and their pleasures as well as someone else's and this is true for both men and women. In any case, receptor partner is a fantasy concept because the anatomically receptive may also require assertive motion to get the stimulation maximally erotic. The idea that intercourse is a domination and reception, an active one and a passive one, is a fantasy about intercourse. When a woman takes her own control of her pleasure after the male insertion, and is active and moves in order to stimulate herself in the way she needs, that is an active process. When a woman inserts her finger into the man, and is excited by it, it is the same as when the man does it to her. The idea that men are always naturally dominant and woman submissive is wrong. Both can be both. Both have always been both. In different ways. In the same way.

Domination seduction seduces/forces the sub to excitement that is seen by the dom as being withheld by the sub; an excitement that is exciting, even irresistible to the sub; a domination and dominator that is irresistible. But this is also usually true of the submissive who is irresistible to the dom. Both feel specially chosen, especially valued. Ultimately, it's about possession, special possession, and the rights and obligations, the anxieties and fears, the loses and anxieties to be repaired, that come with that.

In the continuum of psychodynamics, the evidence for where on the spectrum is any given patient, the exact mixture and relationship of love to aggression, is to be found in the fantasy and their associations which can reveal their unconscious motivations, fears and pleasures. To understand meaning, understand the emotional story which is often hidden in the details of the conscious sensual enactment experiences. This is why the sensuous details are so important. The sensuous lustful experience details are conscious and preconscious. The full conflicted motivation is unconscious. Therefore a therapeutic technique is needed that will access that. This is why psychoanalysis and psychodynamic psychotherapy are such powerful instruments.

The domination submission sexual scene starts in the relationship, from the very beginning. It lies dormant in the attachment attitude. This attitude is enacted in the relationship. A male patient says if the woman, on a first date, leans across the car seat to unlock the door from the inside for him after she gets in, she will have sex with him. True or not, it is an illustration of the derivative indicias at play in the relationship immediately.

In the broad spectrum of BDSM relationships, are two seemingly opposite types of dominants. One is the stern and firm commander, the other is the seductive and soothing receiver. There are two corresponding submissive types. One is the rebellious and counter phobic pseudo independent who needs to be commanded and the other is the anxious but interested one who needs to be reassured. The rebellious submissive provokes the commander and the anxious submissive seduces the seducer. The first indicates I dare you and the second says perhaps you are the one who can help me. The first is afraid to lose control but then yields it to the dominant who is in control because the commander seems to know how to keep things in control and indeed, the seemingly out of control sexual scene will be carefully scripted. The second always feels out of control in the sense of lost, and is always looking for someone to take charge. The first needs commands and the second needs gentleness during the initial phase. There are often combinations. Both are looking for belonging by being owned, as indicated by being told what to do.

Each announces themselves because their personality attitude is displayed and revealed in their interactions, in their facial expressions, in their tone of voice, in their presentation of posture. All of which reveals the attitude. Any or all may be arousal levers. If intense, they probably take their place in the excitement phase of the arousal cycle. All this applies regardless of the sexual orientation of the participants.

These details of display are arousal levers of sensory emotion thing presentations, if the sequence is a fetish enactment. Elements of this scenario may be part of the usual erotic interaction but becomes a fetishized interaction, or more so a fetish enactment, when the enactment is not just a pleasurable erotic augmentation of the person to person relationship but a required, stereotyped drama that is the most or only meaningful relationship and more important than the person. Then the person is merely an actor in the drama.

For the dominator or dominatrix, it's about ownership and the rights of an ownership type of attachment bond. One of the rights is control and command, request and demand. The question is how much of the relationship outside of the sexual scene are these dynamics played out and how fixed, how rigid, how stable, how angrily. As the relationship is more and more captured, as the domination and anger gets more and more, the entire relationship becomes an enactment and may move toward the near psychotic end of the ego spectrum; fantasies made real not just in the mind of the dominator or dominatrix but also in the real relationship. Then how much of that is reassurance against anxiety and how much of it is the control of love versus venting of aggression will determine in part the emotional stability of the relationship. For the analyst, therefore, it's not the sex that is so crucial. It's the nonsexual real relationship. It's the ego function.

Sadomasochism

Domination is about control. Sadism is about enjoyment of another's pain and suffering, physical or emotional. The motivation is different. The amount and purpose of aggression is different. The love issue is different. The bond is different. This is why it is probably erroneous to put them in the same category, BDSM. But the term may have some utility because many cases are mixed and the amount of aggression varies, not only between individuals but within one individual over time as a vicissitude of the relationship. At the extreme, there is instability in the system with the need to prove over and over the power and control dynamic by increasing the sadism of the domination. But most are stable in the requirements and the repetition of the same stereotyped position is all that is required. The difference depends on the malignancy of the narcissistic dynamic in the personality disorder of the dominator, and the malignancy of the masochist dynamic in the personality disorder of the submissive.

In the malignant form, the aggression must escalate because the edge of the envelope is where the thrill is and when either party becomes inured and accepting, the envelope must be extended to rekindle the excitement until either the biology and/or the psychology becomes impossible and the relationship collapses and the attachment breaks. Malignancy means relentless, must always go one step further. Malignancy means that the charge, the peak excitement, is the moment of complete submission and once that is achieved it seems accepted and therefore routine and therefore the excitement envelope must be moved, requiring more pain, because without risk to the relationship there can be no excitement. How much more will the submissive accept. Eventually this destroys the relationship. Hence the term "malignant." It is sad malignancy because the entire enactment is fundamentally to control the fantasy of inevitable loss, which the behavior eventually precipitates. The patient feels mastery at a price instead of helpless at a price. Since the loss seems inevitable, better to feel the master of it than victim of it. But the loss may be painful and may precipitate a severe depression and the sadistic self may still be devastated.

A variant of this is the sociopathic betrayer. The sadism is about betrayal and the emotional suffering of the object. Their hope is betrayed. Their commitment is betrayed. Their loyalty is betrayed. Their attachment is betrayed. If this is conscious and enjoyed in the betrayer, it is the definition of sociopathy. It can be mixed with varying degrees of physical pain infliction, from none to a lot. The emotional pain can be even more painful.

The submissive, often called the masochist, does not usually feel a lack of self or an alienation. They don't usually feel a joyful pleasure but rather a resigned goodness. They feel a special attunement with the dominator and often defend his behavior to others. They feel a special self goodness at their empathy with the dominator. Theirs is a masochist gift of the self and, albeit given with sad dismay and regret depending on the amount of aggression in the dominator, it is also given with hope and charity. It is an about love. It may be proof of their love and lovableness and an offering of affirmation to the lovableness of the dominator. For them, it is an unconscious marker of a secure attachment. The masochistic attachment seems to them to be a secure attachment because it seems to be so needed by the dominator even though never acknowledged.

For some, the masochistic position has the dominant meaning of punishment and it is a sense of guilt that leads them into it. As one said, "the punishment I get is less than the punishment I think I deserve." The conscious punishment deserved may be about aggression or denigration or withholding or teasing but the unconscious guilt may be rather a self-blame for the feeling of not being good enough to be and have been lovable as is. But they sexualize the punishment, which then has a primary, conscious, lustful motive. It becomes an exciting conscious masturbation fantasy and enactment. The meaning is, if they can't be desired for who they are perhaps they can be desired for sex.

Hatred and Criminality

There are two types. In one type, the sadism is a requirement for sexual arousal and orgasm. In the other, sex is merely a sociopathic excuse for sadism unrelated to a requirement of sexual arousal. Key is whether the aggression is conscious and linked specifically to the arousal cycle or whether the aggression is not eroticized and sex is merely the excuse and the setting. The masturbation fantasy gives the clearest view of any eroticization; its dynamics, functions and relationships. In terms of their dangerousness and cruelty, whether or not it is eroticized may be a distinction without a significant difference. The sociopathic ones, cold and without conscience, can be very dangerous, as dangerous as the compulsive sexual sociopathic sadists.

Chapter 9

Treatment

This chapter will discuss special aspects of psychodynamic psychotherapy and psychoanalysis that pertain to sexual experience and to patients who have a fetish or fetish enactments. Presupposed is knowledge of basic psychodynamic technique in the treatment of symptom and of personality. It comes from the point of view of modern ego psychology, which focuses on the ego organizations of symbolic representations of affect as described in previous chapters. These symbolic representations contain the affect ideas of object relations and psychodynamic conflicts and compromises.

Etiology

Basic to treatment is illness; diagnosis and etiology. This is because the illness leaves its characteristic signature on affect content and the ego function organization of structure. Diagnosis includes any illnesses and includes diagnosis of any associated ego dysfunctions. Diagnosis of ego dysfunctions requires careful observation of mental phenomenology: how the ego processes information, including concepts, affects, percepts and their relationships and organization.

Fetish and fetish enactments are conditions in which the ego is locked in a state of rigid concrete lustful representations. The representations have intense sensory affect validity. They have sexualization and boundary porosity, both to external stimuli and to internal affect. Because of the intensity, boundary capacity between internal representation and external reality relatively fails with a resultant push into and use of reality experience for the emotional experience of resulting symbolic representations which are symbolic alterations of reality. The symbolic alterations of reality like all symbolic representations, are symbolic representations of percepts-affect concepts. They are sensory emotional experiences.

It is interesting to see how often these sexual phenomena occur in the setting of ego disorganization and executive function problems that influence the complex ego synthesizing function of symbolic representation. The differential includes attention deficit disorder, certain types of learning

DOI: 10.4324/9780429491733-10

disabilities and executive dysfunctions that involve concrete representation and failures of integration. Similar effects can be seen with bipolar disorder and major depressive disorder especially those that begin in childhood or adolescence. Different illnesses affect ego functions resulting in executive dysfunctions.

Anything that disrupts ego boundaries, decreases ego synthetic capacities, increases affect storms, increase sensitivity to sensory stimulation and overstimulation, including sexual stimulation, may predispose to intense sexuality, to sexualization and to erotic sensual thing presentation representations. The biological causes are affective illness and various executive dysfunctions. The psychological causes are insecurity or abuse in the context of dependency relationships, especially in naturally intense or sensitive children. This is true especially if attachment trauma or biological illness hits during increased sexual intensity phases of development or when personality defenses and ego integration processes or symbolic function of the ego are forming. When a child is emotionally abandoned or abused or overstimulated, and often all three, the emotional response challenges ego functions like organization, logic, emotion modulation and flexible representation capacity and may thus interfere with development.

An often overlooked aspect of trauma is not the acute trauma but the ongoing, lower intensity but constant so-called strain trauma or micro trauma. Particularly relevant are small but continuous emotional abandonments and cruelties and attitudinal impositions that form a context in which a child tries to grow. It results in anxieties, sadness, insecurities and angers that are hard to identify and localize but may become represented and played out in relationships and in symbolic sexual representations thereafter. They may be reawakened by any intensity in emotional relationships, including sexuality, or by a growing commitment. When these attachment anxieties are awakened by sexuality, they become symbolically represented by sexual experience.

These strain traumas may be represented by real, acute traumas. They gain added emotional power to damage because they uncannily represent the continuous strain trauma now in a reality-based conscious memory. It is part of the definition of the screen memory. It has the power to represent yet hide and defend against the more crippling, ongoing emotional strain trauma.

The illnesses and traumas must be treated. But a major explanation is left out so far. That has to do with why the trauma is sexualized. Why is it that sex becomes a defense?

The shift to sexualization involves the ego. There is increased susceptibility to all excitement with any affect if ego boundaries are more porous or if affect intensity tends to be great and if the ego is immature in the solidity of it boundaries and the reliability of reality processing and emotion modulating ego functions. The abilities to boundary, to modulate, to abstract and synthesize is particularly important. If intensity is great or if ego boundary function is poor, then sexual excitement will condense with other intense affect representations, especially in certain phases of development. Phases that are vulnerable because of sexual intensity in normal development are the two-year-old aggression excitement phase, the Oedipal, the late latency and pre- and later-adolescent phases.

The traumatic intensity dynamic may be reawakened during sex because sex so easily symbolizes object relationships and so quickly, due to its intensity and spread, awakens many emotions and their object relations. The physicality of sex and the interactional physiognomy, make it an ideal symbolic representation for the to and fro, give-and-take of attachment bonding of relationships.

Because sex is pleasurable, it is natural to attempt to use it to self soothe. If the self-soothing involves the soothing of trauma then of course that trauma or its derivatives will be pictured in the sexual fantasy. Then the sexual arousal cycle can be used to try to alter the most traumatic aspects. This is done by the sexualization pleasure and the minor but crucial altering of the story so that there is a soothing attitudinal change brought on by the intense sexual attachment.

Important in etiology is the reality of childhood relationships. There may be abuse, physical or emotional, seduction, physical or emotional, or both. Such abuse has its effect on the development and functions of ego-organizing processes because of the challenge of affect intensity. It also has its effect on self-esteem. Abuse is a traumatic object relationship. It abuses the growth and development potential and special uniqueness and value of the victim. Giving further added strength to the trauma effect is if the issue approaches in reality an issue of survival, either physical, emotional or both. Now we can see the tenacity and motivation for sexual themes such as masochism. Masochism is easier to understand if emotional survival or adaptation depended upon it.

The exact mixture of active traumatic acute episodes and different types of emotional abandonment trauma, chronic strain trauma, will determine the specific treatment. Condensations of traumatic neurosis and psychoneurosis are common, to varying extents. Fear is about reality. Anxiety is about worry. This determines treatment techniques. Exact mixtures of ego assets and dysfunctions will also determine treatment.

General Recommendations for Understanding Sexual Experience

The basic principle in treatment is to understand that it is called sexual experience because it is the individual's experience of sex that is crucial. People bring their own meanings to sexual acts and thoughts. Sexual acts and thoughts are universal. Meaning is individual and unique. The meaning of the same sexual act differs from person to person.

Because sex is so intense, major aspects of it are conscious. One can therefore hear a fairly detailed report. The technique is to ask! Then the technique is to help people understand any shame they have that prevents them from telling. Then there is the exploration of meaning. There are many meanings in the manifest content. Further information can be gained by asking for elaborations of those aspects. Meaning is most clear in the masturbation fantasies. This brings into therapeutic purview the range of conscious and almost conscious aspects of the meaningful fantasy of sexual experience. Associations to specific details will give the more unconscious meanings. This is no different than the technique with any symptom, behavior, fantasy or dream. But often therapists don't ask because of shame in the patient and countertransference feelings in the therapist. A major point of this book is that another reason meaning stays hidden is because it is experienced in the sensory details of the physical experience. Associations to this reality sensory experience is one Royal road to meaning.

Sexual experience can be hard for patients to talk about because of their own conflicted feelings about their sexuality and their sexual fantasies. Shame is a powerful inhibitor and this is triggered by exposure to public view, including the view of the therapist. Most don't tell even their most significant other. This fear of shame, therefore, must be explored and interpreted first. Analyzing the fear before the wish, or the underlying content, which is Freud's rule about defense analysis, will pay off because shame-mediated defenses are basic personality defenses and therefore the analysis in relationship to sex will be helpful in the general analysis of the personality neurosis. This is more important than the sexual fantasy because it is the personality dynamics that drive the sexual enactments. Although shame and guilt are barriers for most people discussing any aspect of their sexual fantasy, those with what they perceive as unusual or forbidden variations may be particularly affected by shame, guilt and fear of exposure. Analyze shame first. Shame is a response of the self to the ego ideal that is represented in the sexual fantasy. That which prohibits is about that which is sought. Both have to do with the ego ideal and the self's reactions to and identifications with it. It is a painful conundrum. A Catch 22. Both are a scourge of shame to the other.

Analysis of Thing Presentation or Other Sensory-Emotional Phenomena

The crucial aspect of sexual sensory emotional phenomena is the sensory qualities of the erotic sensual that have meaning and convey affect concepts. The analysis proceeds from inquiries about the exact sensory details that are so exciting and proceeds to inquiries about the special meaning those exciting sensory qualities have for the self and for the self's fantasy of the object. This can be discovered in answer to inquiry about associations to the sensory experience. The associations will bring to consciousness the full fantasy story of meaning. In the sensory details are the sensory qualities and their associated sensory affects and concepts. The sensory affects are a crucial, perhaps the crucial, aspect of the sexual fantasy. They carry the condensed displacement to details of the associated affect concepts. The capacity of sensory qualities to provide a representational experience of affect and its concepts is the phenomenon of thing presentation in sexual experience. These sensory affect concepts contain the crucial object relations fantasies. Associations will reveal the affect concepts that are the building blocks of the story the sexual fantasy and enactment display.

Treatment of Fetish Phenomena

Recognize the phenomena. Often, it goes un-elicited and overlooked. In today's age, where anything goes, currently everything is normal and accepted. But normal and accepted are not the issue. The issue is meaning. The issue is function. Furthermore, it doesn't matter what the analyst or society feels about the fetish but rather what the patient feels. They may feel shame and guilt and the reassurance that this is normal or even common disappoints rather than reassures because the fetish claim is special and unique. Special and unique is ostensibly about the fetish and the act but more unconsciously about the self and the attachment bond. The fetish in the act symbolically represent many conflicted dynamics, perhaps especially the attachment bond with its pleasures and dangers, its conflicts and avoidances, its wishes and fears, its trusts and potential betrayals. Average and common is therefore diminished and discarded rather than special and treasured.

For deeper understanding, get the details of the fetish, the sensory experience, the act, the object and the motivations or plot. This is because sexual symbolic representations are multi-determined emotional representations and symbolizations where the meaning is transformed into the sensory details of the sexual body of the sexual object and the sexual self and the resulting sexual actions. The crucial details involve not who does what to whom, when and how, but more crucially, after all that is known, why. Start with "and how does that feel." The why of how it feels will reveal the meaning. The details of the fetish and its use and the people involved and how and when their attitude changes, link to the arousal cycle and tell a story wherein the first glimmers of deeper meaning can be found. Crucial to meaning is the decoding of affect and affect ideas that are experienced in the sensory details of the fetish object and its use. Recall that the fetish object has attributes of a person and these must be articulated so that they can be fully comprehended. The fetish is also applied to or is part of the body of another person. The body parts are recruited to play a role of meaning that has to be understood.

The arousal is conscious. The other affects and their concepts are not. The what and the how are conscious. The underlying object relations who and why are not. To reveal the story, get the lust details and ask the emotional significance of those details.

The association to the details of the fetish and the story will reveal the latent story of preconscious plot and motivation. The deeper meaning is to be found in the motivation of that latent story. There are even deeper meanings more unconscious that will emerge in the associations to the associations and later in treatment, in the transference and countertransference. This is how an understanding of the fetish evolves.

The human relations story at the surface and the deeper object relations story that is preconscious and unconscious is where meaning is. There are the motivations and the constraints. The deeper meaning of the object relations story can especially be elicited by asking for the details of the face of the sexual object who is subject to the use of the fetish. Critically important is the change in emotional display as the fetish scene proceeds through the arousal cycle. Crucial changes in facial display reflecting change in attitude of the object to the self can be found at the nodal points of the linked arousal cycle. Nodal points are experienced as sexual when actually they are attitudinal. The changes in the emotional experience of the object as displayed on the face signify a change in their real experience of themselves and of the fetishist. This then produces a change in the real self-experience of the fetishist. It is that change in the self that is the underlying motivation. That is the latent preconscious motivation meaning of the story. Why that is important is part of the unconscious story.

Shame and Guilt

Shame and guilt are fairly ubiquitous in these conditions. Of the two, perhaps shame is the more painful. The shame is about the sexual fixation and the sexual enactment. Examples that are especially true is if there is an excretory pathway or focus; any urethral or anal focus or elements. The conflict between urethral or anal excitement and shame and disgust, the excitement in the aroused state, the disgust and shame in the unaroused state is therefore the necessity to keep the two components, excitement versus disgust, dissociated. The reappearance of the disgust post orgasm is an aspect of the organization of this sexual shame experience. The disgust is about the act and the shame is about the self. But there can also be great shame about any submission fantasy. Shame is a crucial part of the motivation and dissociation of the fetish and enactment, therefore the freezing of the compromise into a stereotypy lest the sexualization and dissociation be disturbed. This may be true of all domination and submission fantasies and enactments because of shame.

When arousal begins, the shame is either dissociated or projected onto the sexual object and may become part of a submission fantasy. In the arousal state, the overcoming of shame is a transmuting of it into a momentary sexual triumph and grandiosity of the self in which the aroused self is impervious because it condenses with the ego ideal instead of being submissive to it, and thereby the self is impervious in the aroused state to superego attack. There may be even a condensation into retaliatory righteousness due to the original traumas.

When the fetish experience becomes enacted, the shame is usually even more because the self is actively involved. The excitement of the self cannot be disguised as merely responsive to the excitement in the aroused sexual other.

But sexual enactments and fantasies are reported to the therapist in the non-aroused state and therefore any discussion meets the headwinds of shame and disgust being triggered. If the analyst could help only with that, it would be doing a tremendous service. Because guilt and shame, superego and ego ideal reactions block access to the sexual experience.

Therefore, the therapist talks first about the patient's attitude toward shame and the disgusting. The use of shame and disgust to disguise and administer moralistic and denigrating attacks of a moralistic superego must be analyzed before the content of shame itself. Only then can shame ease and the underlying sexual enactments and fantasies be revealed in their crucial details for analysis. It is important to remember that shame is an experience of the self with the self and not just with the self and observing other. Shame is a relationship experience of the self with the ego ideal and then, therefore, the superego.

There is also guilt about sexual experience. The guilt is about feared damage to the sexual object and harsh judgment about the self's sexual motivations. Patients tend to see the aggression in the experience. They don't see the defended love. This is because while the aggression causes guilt the love paradoxically causes shame, which is even more painful. The whole sexual enactment is constructed because of the danger of deflated self-esteem in the love scene. If the analyst could help only with that, one would be doing a tremendous service.

Because guilt and shame, superego and ego ideal reactions, block access to the sexual experience and to deeper causal dynamics, guilt and shame are referred to as superego defenses. Shame and guilt over feared damage to the object defends against a deeper shame and guilt about the damaged and aggressive narcissistic self; shame over the deflated self and guilt over the inflated self.

Guilt and shame anxiety are paramount in causing the ego defense of dissociation. Dissociation is then used as another way to avoid the full impact of the anxiety and fear experience. The anxiety is not only about the revealing of the fantasy and behavior and therefore the risk to exposure and resulting shame and guilt, but also the fear of venturing into the memory or enactment of the originally traumatic relationship against which the fetish is designed.

Dissociated means divided up. The original connections are not conscious. These dissociations allow different aspects of the conflict to be maintained unintegrated, each influencing the self in its own way. Dissociation keeps one aspect of the conflict away from the other. This occurs in consciousness. The sexual self is experienced separately from the nonsexual self. The attributes of the two states may be very different. Sometimes it is domination in the sexual scene and submission in normal everyday life. Sometimes it is the same in both but with guilt or shame about the sexual scene but not about the personality attitude and the resulting behavior. To help, one must point out and describe both states and also describe the defensive use. They both can then be analyzed as to their purposes and affect contents. The compromises and personality attitude in this sexual material will lead to the personality attitudes and object relations outside of the sexual scene. This is the soil in which human sexuality grows.

Excitement itself may be disassociated from the self. The excitement and its power over the self and hopefully the other person, is experienced as an aspect of the fetish. Not of the self. Then, the significance of this is often disavowed. The dissociated and the disavowed excitement often must be interpreted as a defense before the content can be analyzed.

All this does not apply to the malignant form of criminal sadism in which there is a marked absence of guilt and even of shame. There is often a condensation of grandiose, sadistic ego ideal and real self-experience that is powerful, relentless and dangerous. When it is truly sexualized, it adds the motivation of sexual release and sexual excitement to the aggression motivation. This is very dangerous. It leads to compulsive reenactments. If they can be treated at all, the best setting would be a therapeutic prison.

Dreams

The advantage a dream brings to treatment is that usually more apparent emotional scenes are revealed. They are revealed both in the iconography of the dream and in its plot as it unfolds. The object relations in the manifest content are clear. That means that the theme of the relationships are clear. If it is also a sexual dream, then you have demonstrated the link.

Usually the fetish scene does not appear in dreams. Perhaps it doesn't have to because it is conscious and enacted. When it does, it usually means the treatment is going well. This is because the ego defenses of dissociation are easing and the fetish is now appearing in the dream theater where symbolization can be more plastic, less fixed, have association links and webs more available, and reveal its deeper meanings. Telling a dream implies a more dispassionate observing ego with less guilt and shame. The dream allows for a me-not me experience; a me observing me. Even though at first the dream is merely a replay, the ego is signaling a change in readiness to explore the symbolization of the fetish and not just its repetition experience as a concrete representation. The dream setting allows the fetish to appear in relationship to its meaningful psychological context. The dream allows the analysis to more easily unpack the fetish into latent dream thoughts. It is now just a dream. New meanings are usually first and most easily, with less resistance, found in the dreamer's emotional reactions to the dream scene. That's the newly revealed experience of the fetish and its meaning.

The analysis of the fetish proceeds from exact description and experience to its use in the arousal cycle. This is part of the exact description of the fetish and fetish enactment fantasy.

But the necessities of the arousal cycle stereotypy, reinforced by intense sexual pleasure, can make it hard to unpack the condensed meanings. In the dream, there may not be that intense arousal and the dreamer may be also the observer not just the actor. Then there can be associations to and thoughts about, not just repetition, of arousal.

Inhibition

Identifying and explicating sexual inhibition is crucial to the analysis of the fetish. Circumventing the inhibition to progression through the arousal cycle and to sexual satisfaction is one of the major goals of the fetish. The inhibition story is in some ways the opposite of the story of the enactment. There is therefore an internal dissociation and repression in the structure that needs to be identified, elucidated, felt and integrated.

The first goal is finding the point of inhibition which the fetish bypasses. The patient must be their own participant observer. The inhibition may be more easily located in a report of a masturbation fantasy. Then, because the only other real person in the room is the patient themselves, the sequence of their inner state and the point of loss of excitement or stall in progression of excitement, is more easily noticeable by them. The inhibition is easier to locate because the fetish inserts itself into the arousal cycle story at a certain point, the point where arousal begins to fail.

Inhibitions are anxieties, fears, guilts, shame, past traumas that are symbolically represented in the point of inhibition of the arousal cycle. The dynamic content of the feared and warded off can be seen in derivative form in the fetish replacement. Free associations will elaborate the themes in both. The transference and countertransference will have the themes. The defenses are personality congruent.

Example

A woman gets very excited until the mid-phase, before inevitability. The excitement then stops. Lubrication ends. The clitoris loses its sensitivity. No orgasm can occur. This happens only with a partner, not in masturbation. In masturbation, at that point, the vibrator takes over and she can go on to orgasm. The fantasy is of using it on her and using it on him. In treatment, the issue of who is in charge and who loses control turns out to be central. She unconsciously experiences interpersonal sex as having to yield to another because of her own excitement with another, raising fears of addiction and loss of power to the other. She isn't aware that it is her own excitement and its power to addict her to him that she fears. Her fantasy of using the vibrator on him is that the other yields to her excitement. It was General Patton who was quoted as saying he didn't want his boys dying for their country. He wanted his boys to make their boys die for their country! The French call an orgasm un petit mort.

The analyst may first focus on the sensuous feeling of the vibrator and her associations to it. It is always hard. It therefore cannot be a measure of her attractiveness. When it vibrates, it seems active, not passive. She turned the vibratory on. She is active. Her vibratory is active. It is hers. She controls it. She likes to squeeze it, hard. She now dominates. Her vibrator is green which reminds her of Kermit the Frog who says it's not easy being green. She fears she is soft to be green, green being her color for arousal. Her feeling of power is not strong enough, not consistent enough to stand up for itself, especially during sex when there is danger of feeling swept away, helpless in the arousal sequence. The dynamics are all condensed in the reliable hardness of the vibrator. It is always available and at her command.

The vibrator seems to symbolically represent qualities of her wished for but insecure phallic power and ideal self. It is this aspect of determination and personality that she yearns for comfortably during sex in her own self but which is insecure. She wishes it but fears it is only in men during sex. But with the vibrator, his phallic power is now her phallic power. It reaffirms her own phallic power. She experiences passion as his passion because of his obvious erection rather than her own passion and her clitoral erection.

Treatment will obviously have to help her with her own feelings of power, not only with her feelings about his power. The vibrator is her power but it is still externalized. The use of the vibrator is not a problem except to the extent that it represents a lack of emotional power in her. But then it is an internal problem not an external problem. One would look for enactments of inhibited assertion in her nonsexual interactions or perhaps her over-domination in such ordinary social interactions, or both. In her interpersonal life, she is both inhibited and abruptly assertive, usually with anger.

Fetish Enactments

Similar rules apply for the psychodynamic psychotherapy and psychoanalysis of fetish enactments as apply to static fetish phenomena. The only difference is the action. Because the units of expression are actions, some symbolic representations progress rapidly through a sequence and the sequence itself is a symbolic representation of object relations attitudes and processes.

The rapid action makes it harder for the patient to see the story because the action sequence disguises the exact specific nodal points where the story is most meaningful and the inhibitions are hidden. Also making observing ego difficult are the same personality traits in the sexual enactment and in their everyday life and therefore also in the telling of the story to the analyst.

The great advantage of enactments over the static form is that the action clearly reveals the story to the analyst. When the story is described to the patient, they cannot avoid recognizing the plot and the themes although the affect may still be repressed and dissociated. In the forward motion of the implied plot, in the interaction of the participants, can be found the theme. In the reactions of the participants can be found the object relations. In the links to the arousal nodes can be found both the inhibition and the peak moments physically and therefore of significance. In the crucial pre-arousal and post-arousal states are the motivations for the sequence and the satisfaction of the conclusion. Even if the early theme seems to be only manipulation or domination for compliance, there is probably a major motivation for the entire sequence that is more unconscious. Probably one meaning of the ecstatic dénouement is the changing of misery into pleasure, and the change in the self-experience from failure to triumph.

But what this means for treatment and for technique is the requirement for the patient to report the enactment in detail. Getting the report involves the understanding and interpretation of dissociation, denials and disavowals, symbolic displacements, guilts, shames and humiliations. This can be difficult because there may be intense and wide dissociations involving the entire self in what is essentially a type of fugue state. Or there may be intense shame experiences that need to be analyzed. Often, personality defenses against that shame must be analyzed first. Therefore, the full report may take years to emerge but during that time much analysis of personality attitude is occurring.

Because action is a reality experience event, because the action is a drama, the drama has the structure of a screen memory where affect validity is intense and validated unconsciously by the in-reality experience. Affect validity is strongly in reality experience, not in emotional experience. The behavior is conscious, the affect is preconscious and the affect concepts of meaning are unconscious.

Object Relations

Fetish enactments are a lustful object relations story. Often left out of the report is the sexual object's reaction to the behavior as displayed on the face and in the attitudes of the sexual object. The need for a change there is the motivation for the action. The goal is to change the day residue of the object's attitude to the self which, however, is the self's projection onto the object in the self's reality mental experience. This paradigm is the enactment.

Therefore the analytic goal is to hear the story not only of what is done but the object's reaction to it and the self's reaction to that. This is the crucial sequence because the goal of the drama is to produce a change in the attitude of the object. This attitude is expressed physically in the object, both sexual response and emotional response, and is to be experienced by the self in the object's real physical experience, but also in their emotional experience. Asking at every step of the story how the sexual object is feeling at that point will help reveal the other half of the story, the sexual object story, often left out from the elaboration of the self-story. Getting the self-view of the changes in the object are crucial in understanding the motivation of the self but it can be the other way around and one gets the object story before the self-story.

The object relations in the lustful story may be collated objects, which need to be understood as separated into their separate plots and subplots. The analysis then helps integrate them into their relationships and syntheses. The sequence usually repeats, directly and in reverse, strain trauma in relationship to a primary object, both feared and wished. The wish is to engage, conquer and seal the security of the attachment bond with the strength of the lustful enactment in the face of attachment fears. The fears will also reveal themselves in the transference and countertransference. If the personality style of the patient is an enactment style, then this dynamic will be enacted in non-sexual ways as well.

Trauma

Acute traumas are assaults, seduction and abandonment. They can be physical. They can be emotional. They are usually consciously remembered because they are obvious events. Many result in obvious damage, physical or emotional or both.

Strain traumas are also called micro traumas. They are usually unconscious. They are the result of continuous abandonments, emotionally, continuous mean-spirited attitudes, in the relationship of parents to children, or siblings. The strain traumas reflect the attitudes of relationships from the inflictor to the recipient. They get repeated in the adaptation of attitudes in object relations of the victim. Ironically, they tend to get enacted by the victim, precipitating an interpersonal repetition of the strain trauma.

Who tends to get over acute trauma? When the acute trauma is not so severe. Also, those without strain trauma. Those without any need to symbolically represent a strain trauma by acute trauma. When the strain trauma is symbolically represented in sexual enactments, the emotional pain is disguised by very positive reinforcing lustful affect, making insight difficult.

The need to repeat is partly the ego's attempt at mastery; as well as to conquer, to avenge, to extract love, to seduce a commitment; to feel valued and special instead of used and discarded. As the analysis proceeds, the strain trauma becomes more and more clear in the transference and countertransference. Becomes more and more clear in the personality adaptations of the patient. It becomes more and more clear in factual memory. Then can come the easing of the repetition compulsion that repeats the strain trauma.

Transitional Objects and Enactments

Transitional objects are halfway between fantasy and reality. Transitional aspects of fetish objects and fetish enactments can be useful to treatment because they are an attempt to use a concrete representation to adjudicate anxiety in fantasy's relationship to the real object. This transitional process, which should be a continuous growth and development process, is frozen. Opening up its meaning, its wishes and fears, may free it to become a new compromise formation at a higher level of organization, free of avoidance of the whole object and the whole relationship. That may release the growth potential of the self. The first step is when one sees plasticity in the fetish and fetish enactment; things start to change there first. But the first steps can be scary for the patient because they may reveal more undisguised forms of the underlying sexual fantasy. These more direct fantasies, sometimes called more primitive, can be the unconscious triggers for the warded off dissociated guilt and shame that is such a feared aspect of these sexual structures. But it is usually easy to demonstrate the corresponding increase and pleasure in the real relationship and in the more complete sexual relationship. Therefore, what is sometimes seen by the therapist as a barrier, the fixed transitional object fetish, should also be seen as an opportunity. The transitional object fetish is a kind of a stalemate but it also is a kind of potential because it is at the intersection of fantasy and reality.

Personality Analysis

Crucial to the analysis is to show the corresponding dynamics in the non-sexual personality attitudes and defenses. Sexual behavioral enactments grow from the soil of personality issues. Trauma adaptations, to both acute and strain trauma, appear most clearly in personality defenses in the object relations of personality attitude. They are also, secondarily expressed in the behavior and the plot of the sexual scene. There are the attitudes toward self and object that are basic to personality. They will not be effectively resolved until personality conflicts and defenses are analyzed.

The analysis involves understanding the personality attitudes that are expressed in the sexual scene, both in their concepts and in their object relations affects and then their defensive functions against developmental traumas of different types. These themes, their concepts and affects, should be described wherever they appear. The attitude will be divided among participants and among different parts of the story and between the story and the self-experiences of the story. The attitudes will also be found in the transference and the countertransference.

They are integrated by pointing them out, opening up their individual stories, and showing how the stories are related to each other, in historical fact and in fantasy, each an integral part of each other and of the larger, integrated story. It is the fantasy story of the enactment that is integrative, although highly disguised.

The key to the analysis of personality is discovering the attitudes and object relations themes organized by these attitudes. These attitudes are the relational compromises of object relations. The attitudes are supra ordinate and involve all mental agencies in organizing object relations and are expressed in enactments of them. The sexual scenes can help in seeing object relations experiences which are so clearly illustrated in the sexual drama. This can help locate the object relations outside the sexual scene in the non-aroused state. The attitude is implied in the behavior and revealed more directly in fantasy and is clearly expressed in the transference and countertransference. For patients who enact, the countertransference maybe the first place for identifying these attitudes because the enactments are not felt by the patient. They are felt by the target of the behavior, for instance, the analyst.

Transference

Treatment of fetish experiences involve special issues of transference and countertransference. The excitement, shame, disapproval, guilt, anger and avoidance may be found in either the transference or the countertransference, and usually both.

Early transferences may be avoided or projected as superego transferences of shame and guilt. Later transferences may be of excitement and paranoid projection of aggression and denigration. Later yet may be the transference of attachment inconsistency and object inconsistency. Later are the whole object syntheses with their projective identifications and introjections. The transference to the good object is more avoided, dissociated and unconscious because of the fears it triggers, until the later phases of treatment when such attachment transferences may become desperate and aching. Then comes the morning of the relationships that were so crucial to growth and development but which were lost, withdrawn, denied, sabotaged or betrayed. This is a very painful mourning because the normal sequence of enshrinement as a blessed object memory isn't possible and because it means revisiting the denigrated self of then. But from this mourning can be rescued the resilient self and a feeling of power and control now as an adult. Then can come a blessed memory of the sanctity and value of the self, not the object, back then. This can be reparative and sustaining.

These transferences are marked by their intensities; either avoided or flooding. The avoidance can be frustrating. Their intensities can be overwhelming.

The analyst comments on these vicissitudes. The goal is to help the patient recognize the phenomena, some of the reasons for it and, most importantly, to be able to control it, both the absence and the flooding. Remember that overwhelming intensity is traumatic for the patient, particularly as a child. Children who are both overstimulated and deprived are particularly vulnerable to the ego dysfunction of modulation capacity. The dysregulation in the adult may not appear only in behavior but in the on off, absence and flooding, of their transference experience.

The treatment must also be directed to personality issues because personality attitudes organize a stable relationship between the person, their conflicts, and their world. It's personality attitudes that organize thematic meanings of life histories. It is therefore to be understood that personality attitude will be directed at organizing and defending against human sexual experience especially when the self considers it weird, wrong, bad, or shameful. Personality attitude then becomes a defense that must be interpreted in order to get to a report of the sexual material and to be able to analyze it. The defense will be typical of the personality style.

The hysteric patient tends to give feelings, emotionality, rather than an actual description of sexual fantasy or behavior. Easier and perhaps first to appear is a description of the behavior but often ascribed to the other person as motivator and orchestrator, not themselves. They may have two simultaneous reactions to their talking about it. The first is in their description, which are full of disavowal of significance or even denial or omission of fact. The second is the simultaneous excitement arousal in their expression and inherent in their emotionality. If inquired about, they could more easily grasp the anger component of it. The sexual arousal component, while perhaps obvious to the observer, is often denied or disavowed. It is this denial or disavowal, even if obvious, that makes the experience of treating them a kind of chasing after them. But this can be noted by the analyst as an organizing, identifying interpretation of personality style used as defense.

The obsessive patient may be the opposite. Lots of details and facts but denial and disavowal of the emotions and emotional meanings. They may be aware only of a general discomfort and vague disgust rather than the full force of their guilt and shame. But they may be aware of their shame and that is the place to begin. The therapist then asks about the affect. Perhaps the shame is a feeling; of disgust. That disgust feeling has certain associated ideas.

Their disgust is an important expression of their moralistic attitude. It is a real problem for them not just in their sexual experience, in their sexual desire, but in their relationships in general. The therapist doesn't challenge that so much as engage it and help the patient spell it out in detail so that its exaggerated and inhumane and unrealistic nature become clear. This is what they suffer from. This is what they tend to impose on others. They impose it on their own reactions to their own sexuality and to the sexual desires themselves. It is here the therapy can help them so much.

The paranoid patient has trust issues in revealing their sexual acts and desires. They experience themselves as ok with it but not the listener. The first step of treatment is to understand that they are feeling this way and therefore withholding. The second step is to help them see that they have feelings about sex that they then assume to be the attitude of the therapist. Some readily agree and say that it's only natural that others should feel that way. It is helpful to analyze why the location of the disapproval is in the other and not in the their self. After more fully elaborating the projection to the real object, it will be easier to help the patient locate one of the origins of that to their own self attitudes. Both the obsessive and the paranoid are frightened of any aggressive component in their sexuality. The obsessive fear is moral judgment while the paranoid fear is retribution by the object.

Narcissistic patient feels a combination of grandiosity and denigration, that their sexual acts and preferences are so unique and special, while at the same time feeling and fearing denigration because of them. Those who overcome their shame and guilt in grandiose, triumphant sexual aggression are the hardest to treat. Those who suspend shame and guilt during the act and then are wracked by shame and guilt afterwards are easier to treat. This is obviously so because they internalize the neurotic reaction and suffer from it and so therefore it is a symptom. That neurotic reaction to themselves seems superego justified. Both types of narcissistic patient are oblivious to the object's experience, which in the case of the bully is not pleasant but in the case of the seducer or even the hesitant, passive hopeful, may be pleasant. And neither appreciates the possibility of an independent emotional life of the object. The bully is contemptuous of it. The hesitant seducer, frightened of any aggression, can't imagine the object's desire. There is an intermediate form in which there is the assumption of a mirroring relationship in which the sexual object will be the exactly desired complement to be met with denigrating disappointment when that turns out not to be true, even in details that should be minor.

Masochistic patients claim imposed suffering and suddenly demand that the analyst agree and share in that suffering, both vicariously in the listening and actually in some details of the proposed analytic treatment contract. The analyst must be able to empathically describe this and to inquire about its deeper motivation. Here in the relationship in the room is the evidence for the subtle dynamics of suffering, noble suffering, in the patient's sexual relationships.

The sadistic patient's transference may be a continuous attempt at leverage to gain the upper hand and cause emotional discomfort as a power trip. There in the relationship is the same dynamic as in their sexual fantasy and sexual behavior. This can be calmly described and interpreted as a comfort maneuver for the patient and inquiry can be made about why such a comfort maneuver is needed and comfortable for the patient. This will start the analysis of the pleasurable power in the fantasy of inflicting suffering on another.

The advantage to personality analysis for sexual problems is the ability to help the patient understand their experience. It is also to help them understand their attitude in general, and its interpersonal consequences, which can free them in their general relationships not just in their sexual.

Countertransference

Countertransference feelings are a major reason such sexual material does not get analyzed. If there is a transference-countertransference of excitement, a stalemate may result with high affect intensity. If there is denial, repression and avoidance of the transference-countertransference, the experience is one of boredom with a low affect intensity stalemate.

The main issue for treatment is whether the analyst can experience the countertransference. Can the analyst experience and realize boredom as a defense, in the patient and the analyst, that is being used as an avoidance of something emotionally intense? Can the analyst be excited and use it for empathic interpretations? The countertransference is the emotional connection required for all analytic treatments that seek transformation. It can create the state of transitional imagination, with the analysis as the transitional object, wherein lies the possibility of the exploration of deep meaning and of growth and development change. This is no different than any analytic treatment but the analysis of sexual contents requires a special holding capacity in the analyst. This requires tolerance in the analyst of sexual excitement and the fantasies and counterreactions triggered.

The most disruptive countertransference reactions are superego reactions of shame and guilt. A marker of this is sometimes disgust and repulsion. When this is only vaguely conscious, the avoidances and subtle attacks it triggers, may not be noticed. It requires a therapist well analyzed who is comfortable with their sexuality and aware of their own reactions against it.

The other disruptive countertransference reactions are the opposite of guilt and shame reactions. These are the enacting reactions in which the excitement of the analyst is gratified. The obvious and most destructive are sexual relations between therapist and patient. But there are derivatives in over-soliciting and ingratiating by the therapist. One way this is expressed is to maintain an idealizing transference by never confronting the ambivalence. Another way is to idealize the sensual emotional details that are so arousing and to focus on them at the expense of exploring their meaning. The meaning is avoided because the meaning is nonsexual and not arousing. Therefore, the analyzing of it is a deprivation for the therapist.

Because the therapist is hopefully better and more completely analyzed than the patient, the countertransference may be reasonably accurate and may precede the patients conscious awareness of the material by days or years. The clinical art is timing. The analyst uses the countertransference to reassure themself that something is happening and that the patient may be arriving at this material. Countertransference can therefore be a guide to the analyst about what is missing in the patient's material. It can be a guide not only to the arousing sexual fantasies but also to the reactions against them of guilt and shame. To discover in their self, the analyst, guilt and shame about sexual arousal and certain fantasies is an offer of growth and development for the analyst.

The danger is, however, that it is purely the analyst's material evoked by the arousal. This then would leave the analyst very far astray. Countertransference is therefore best used as a possible indicator. The analyst keeps the counter-transference fantasies in mind as the material progresses looking for confirmation or non-confirmation in the patient's material. Ultimately, we care what we feel only if it is a help to understanding what the patient feels. Any meaning for us is very secondary to our main job of understanding their meaning to them.

Countertransference varies according to the developmental phase of the analysis. It will give clues to the development of the sexual representations. It may be the boring object; the exciting object; the frightening object; the terrorizing or traumatizing object; the scornful, contemptuous object; or the asexual, safe and uninteresting object. There may be various derivative enactments along the way. The crucial issue is can the analyst be excited but behaviorally contained and verbally articulate? Can the analyst be bored without disinterest and able to articulate that? The advantage to countertransference is the information to be gained. The disadvantage is the temptation to action or to avoidance. Occasional countertransference dreams can be very helpful in understanding the evolution of the dynamics. Countertransference is a concomitant or concordant version of the transferences. Action carries the danger of a projective identification to the real, object and then the object in reality.

Psychoanalyze all action phenomena as if they were reports of a dream where the images, behavior and action processes are symbolic representations of attitudes of the self and the other. The sensory details are often crucial because they include crucial dynamics and motivational meanings and because they may coincide with nodes of wished for state change. Point to the details and get associations to them. These details are condensed displacements of conflict and compromise illustrated in the arousal cycle.

Don't be fooled by the sex qua sex. Sex is more than Sex. The treatment is the treatment of attitude and of strain trauma not only of acute trauma and of subsequent conflict. The treatment is the treatment of action oriented ego styles and action traumatizing families. The treatment is the treatment of ego deficits that make expression along fantasy and verbal channels sluggish but along behavioral channels immediate. The treatment is of co-morbid mood disorders that intensify all elements and stress the affect behavior boundary.

It is the transference to the personality issues that are perhaps more difficult than the sexual material. With the hysteric patient, one has the feeling of
constantly chasing after them and trying to pin them down to what exactly
they feel and what the exact happening details are. If this is enacted they
respond as if they are being sexually attacked. Because it is in the context of
sexual excitement, there can be countertransference of rape fantasies that
can be very disquieting and unpleasant if not understood. Because the effect
of the chasing after is to cause feelings of lack of power and effectiveness in
the therapist, there can be fantasies of sexual acts that reverse this equation.
These fantasies can cause shame and guilt in the analyst. If these fantasies
are very defended against, they may appear in countertransference dreams
which can be very helpful. The dangers of too immediate and too direct
interpretation of warded off sexual content and actions is that the patient
experiences the origin as in the analyst. Then the analyst is seen as the sexual
one who aggressively advances a theory about it.

Countertransference with the obsessive patient may be boredom, which
can be quite confounding considering that the obsessive is talking about sex.
But it is a cold and clinical rendition without emotional meaning or even
excitement. The analyst in listening may tend to fill in the emotion and the
excitement in which case they may feel uncomfortably out of sync with the
patient. If the analysis has progressed to the point of uncovering the beginning of the moralistic defensive layer and the ego's identification with the
rigid superego, then the analyst may be in danger of an angry contemptuous attack if they are perceived as accepting the patient's sexual fantasy and
enactments. Better to first empathize with the suffering involved in the moralistic judgment against themselves and to help elaborate it out of the preconscious into full consciousness and secondary process. One is then able to
confront the irrational in the hyper moralism.

Both hysteric and the obsessive countertransference is a danger to the analyst experiencing arousal. But then there is less data for the analyst to use in
understanding both the sexual desire and moralistic aggression against it.

The countertransference of the paranoid patient is usually hesitancy and
anxiety about precipitating an angry, moralistic, paranoid attack. The analyst
treads carefully with such patients but can begin to point out that phenomena. The analyst can say that he hesitates to comment on certain areas less
they upset the patient and make him angry. The analyst then names the exact
area that has come into view. Now comes the opportunity to analyze that
paranoid personality defense which is even more important than the sexual.
This may have to be done before each new step. But it can then be shown,
through its repetition, to be a general attitude stance which brings with it, its
own impairment in relationships. This depends on the analyst being able to
be aware and articulate, without fear, his fear of the patient.

Countertransference with narcissistic patients grapples with early shame
around superiority and inferiority and which is which, the analyst or the

patient. This is especially so if the topic is considered shameful by the patient, as is often the case with their sexual fantasy and behavior. Then comes the Catch 22 in which reassurance triggers denigration and lack of reassurance triggers shame. Again, the technique has to do with describing this. The problem is wrestling with any anger in the countertransference that is responsive to the patient's early denigration. But with healthier narcissistic patients, the countertransference may be to the patient's idealizing transference and the temptation for grandiosity on the part of the analyst. This would be naïve not only in its reality but its failure to understand that denigration will surely follow and that the task is neither to be intimidated nor aggrandized but to describe and interpret.

The countertransference with masochistic patience is either to engage in their suffering with great concern and settle on a signing of an unconscious masochistic contract demanding suffering on the part of the analyst or to feel anger at it. Better to remain unencumbered and to feel instead a righteous anger against the forces of evil that cause the patient suffering. Later in treatment it may be anger against the patient's morality for causing suffering at the hands of their own masochism. Unconscious countertransference anger and suffering imposed upon the analyst by the patient's masochism can result in a kind of sadistic aggression in emotional reactions by the analyst with subtle aggressive behaviors and withholdings.

The countertransference to the sadistic patient is anger or withdrawal. Again, the key is to recognize this and to try to put it into words for the patient. If one is successful, the sadistic patient may be delighted at their power to elicit such reactions. This can then be interpreted. It becomes a dramatic in the moment demonstration of the lack of concern for the object. This can lead to an exploration of the relative overpowering of love by aggression in the sadistic patient's use of the masochistic object. It is well into analytic treatment before the sadistic patient's own vulnerable, yearning and potentially masochistic self comes into view which a grandiose sadistic self denies and hates.

But perhaps the most difficult part of the countertransference is when desire is stirred in the analyst. This can be most upsetting when it is felt as an actual genital arousal and it is to patient fantasy or behavior that is ego alien to the analyst. Any strong sensory emotional feelings or even thing presentation experiences will make it even more upsetting. Now comes an opportunity for the analyst to understand better their own superego prohibitions and retaliation against aspects of sex and sexual experience. What is upsetting in the moment can be a growth experience longer run for the analyst with great improvement in their analytic instrument and in their own growth and development. But the experience can be upsetting and accounts, perhaps, for many failures to engage and analyze the gritty details of sexual experience. It also, of course, partly accounts for some of the boundary crossing sexual enactments between patient and analyst that are so devastating.

Closing Remarks

General advisories would be don't push, don't avoid, don't be premature, don't be delayed, don't minimize, don't exaggerate, don't enact. Put everything into words as soon as it feels possible according to the rule of therapeutic tact. This can only be felt. The rate limiting step is not only the rigidity of the patient's defenses but the capacity of the analyst both for empathy and for articulation from this empathic stance.

The treatment isn't trying to eliminate the sexual enactment. It is trying to help the patient understand and therefore to deepen its meaning. The result at first will be an evolution in the complexity of the enactment and its experience. The goal is to include in it an experience of the whole object and to have that intensify the love component and the security component. Then it will be easier for it to become a transitional experience of growth and development. Questions for the analysis of sexual enactment are – is there only stereotypy or is there plastic representation? Is it a stagnant process or a transitional process of growth and development? Is there hope in it at as well as anxiety and terror? Is it for mastery or destructive addiction? Is it voluntary or compulsive? Does it increase bonding or dissociation? Is it an enhancement or a degradation of the person and of sexuality?

Be patient. Analyses of these conditions takes time. The robust analysis will have many vicissitudes. And even a little help at better adaptations within whole object relations in reality, is a lot of help. When the fetish experience engages a whole self and whole object, becomes less fixed, evolves in its contents, is tenderly held, is seen as a uniquely loving contribution of the willing and participatory object, when it enhances the self and the object as a symbol of special devotion, when it is in fantasy and transitional experience and not just required in reality experience, then can the analysis be said to be successful. Then can other sexual pleasures less fraught with neurotic meaning also be enjoyed. Then the real relationship can be freer and more loving.

To integrate their understanding of their own deeply felt experience has a chance of bringing peace of mind. To understand the fetish and fetish enactment and personality attitudes, the derivatives in nonsexual behavior, the beginnings in childhood relationships and particularly strain traumas, provides a self-observing capacity, catalyzing integration. The treatment can thus open the possibility of a more fulfilling life because what it is that is really being sought may then be really found; in imagination and then perhaps in relationships; secure, loving relationships.

Finis

Bibliography

Aarons, Z. A. (1959). A study of a perversion and an attendant character disorder. *PsaQ.*, 28, 481–492.

Ahlers, C. J., Schaefer, G. A., Mundt, I. A., Roll, S., Englert, H., Willich, S. N., & Beier, K. M. (2011). How unusual are the contents of paraphilias? Paraphilia-associated sexual arousal patterns in a community-based sample of men. *The Journal of Sexual Medicine*, 8, 1362–1370. doi:10.1111/j.1743-6109.2009.01597.x

Akhtar, S., & Kramer, S. (1977). *Intimacy and Infidelity: Separation Individuation Perspectives*. Jason Aronson, Northvale, NJ.

Akhtar, S., & Kramer, S. (eds.) (1996). *Intimacy and Infidelity: Seperation-Individuation Perspectives*. Jason Aronson, Northvale, NJ.

Alison, L., Santtila, P., Sandnabba, N. K., & Nordling, N. (2001). Sadomasochistically oriented behavior: Diversity in practice and meaning. *Archives of Sexual Behavior*, 30, 1–12.

Alperin, R. M. (2001). Barriers to intimacy: An object relations perspective. *Psa Psych*, 18(1), 137–156.

Angel, K. (2012). *Unmastered: A Book on Desire, Most Difficult to Tell Farrah*. Strauss & Giroux, New York, NY.

Angel, K. (2021). *Tomorrow Sex Will Be Good Again*. Verso Books, London.

Arafat, I. S., & Cotton, W. L. (1974). Masturbation practices of males and females. *Journal of Sex Research*, 10(4), 293–307.

Bacon, R., & Briken, P. (eds.) (2021). *Compulsive Sexual Behavior Disorder, A Clinician's Guide*. APA Press, Washington, DC.

Bak, R. C. (1953). Fetishism. *J. Amer. Psychoanal. Assn.*, 1, 285–298.

Bak, R. C. (1968). The phallic woman: The ubiquitous fantasy in perversions. *Psychoanal. St. Child*, 23, 15–36.

Bak, R. C. (1973). Being in love and object loss. *Int. J. Psycho-Anal.*, 54, 1–8.

Bak, R. C. (1974). Distortions of the concept of fetishism. *Psychoanal. St. Child*, 29, 191–214.

Blizard, R. A. (2001). Masochistic and sadistic ego states: Dissociative solutions to the dilemma of attachment to an abusive caretaker. *Journal of Trauma & Dissociation*, 2, 37–58.

Blos, P. (1966). *On Adolescence*. Free Press, New York, NY.

Blum, H. P. (ed.) (1977). *Female Psychology*. International Universities Press, Madison, CT.

Calarusso, C. A. (2012). The central masturbation fantasy in heterosexual males across the life cycle: Masturbation fantasies across the normality-pathology spectrum. *JAPA J Am Psychoanal Assoc*, 5, 917–948.

Celebrate, A. (2014). *Erotic Revelations: Clinical Applications and Perverse Scenarios*. Routledge, London & New York, NY.

Celenza, A. (2014). *Erotic Revelations*. Routledge, Abington-on-Thames.

Chasseguet-Smirgel, J. (ed.) (1970). *Female Sexuality-New Psychoanalytic Views*. University of Michigan Press, Ann Arbor, MI.

Chasseguet-Smirgel, J. (1984). *Creativity and Perversion Free*. Association Books, London.

Chasseguet-Smirgel, J. (1999). The devil religion: Some reflections on the historical and social meanings of the perversions. *J. Clin. Psychoanal.*, 8(3), 381–400.

Chivers, M. L., Roy, C., Grimbos, T., Cantor, J. M., & Seto, M. C. (2014). Specificity of sexual arousal for sexual activities in men and women with conventional and masochistic sexual interests. *Archives of Sexual Behavior*, 43, 931–940.

Coen, S. J. (1985). Perversion as a solution to intrapsychic conflict. *J. Amer. Psychoanal. Assn.*, 33S(Supplement), 17–57.

Coles, P. (1988). Aspects of perversion in anorexic bulimic disorders. *Psa. Psychotherapy*, 3(2), 137–147.

Damon, W. (2003). Dominance, sexism, and inadequacy: Testing a compensatory conceptualization in a sample of heterosexual men involved in SM. *Journal of Psychology & Human Sexuality*, 14, 25–45.

De M'Uzan, M. (1973). A case of masochistic perversion and an outline of a theory. *IJP*, 54: 455–467.

Deleuze, G. (ed.) (1989). *Masochism: Coldness & Cruelty*; Sacher-Masoch, L. *Venus in Furs*. Zone Books, New York, NY.

Diamond, D., Blatt, S. J., & Lichtenberg, J. D. (eds.) (2007). *Attachment and Sexuality*. Routledge, New York, NY, London.

Dor, J. (2001). *Structure and Perversions* (Tr.) Susan Fairfield. Other Press, New York, NY.

Eigen, M. (2002). *Lust*. Wesleyan University Press, Middletown, CN.

Eisler, K. (1960). Notes on the problems of technique in the psychoanalytic treatment of adolescence, with some remarks on perversions. *IJP*, 41, 651–661.

Ellis, H. (1905). *Studies in the Psychology of Sex*, vols. 1 & 2. Kingsport Press, Kingsport, TN.

Ellis, H. (1906). *The Psychology of Sex*. FA Davis & Co., Philadelphia, PA.

Ellis, H. (1923). *Studies in the Psychology of Sex*. FA Davis, Philadelphia, PA.

Escoffier, J. (2020). Every detail counts: Robert Stoler, perversion and the production of pornography. *Psychoanalysis and History*, 22, 35–52.

Esthope, A. (1989). *Poetry and Fantasy*. Cambridge University Press, New York, NY.

Fairbairn, W. R. D. (1952). *Psychoanalytic Studies of the Personality*. Routledge, London.

Fenichel, O. (1945). *The Psychoanalytic Theory of Neuroses*. WW Norton, Inc., New York, NY.

Files, R. (1956). *Erogeneity and Libido*. IUP, New York, NY.

Filippini, S. (2005). Perverse relationships, the perspective of the perpetrator. *IJP*, 86, 755–773.

Fisher, S. (1973). *The Female Orgasm: Psychology, Physiology*. Fantasy Basic Books, New York, NY.

Fogel, G., Lane, F. M., & Liebert, R. S. (1986). *The Psychology of Men*. Basic Books, New York, NY.

Fogle, G. I., & Myers, W. A. (1991). *Perversions and Near Perversions in Clinical Practice*. Yale University Press, New Haven, CT.

Freedman, A. (1978). Psychoanalytic study of an unusual perversion. *JAPA*, 26, 749–777.

Freud, A. (1963). The concept of developmental lines. *The Psychoanalytic Study of the Child*, 18, 245–265.

Freud, S. (1905). *Three Essays on the Theory of Sexuality* (Ed.) James Strachey. Standard edition, vol. 7. The Hogarth Press, London.

Freud, S. (1915). *The Unconscious* (Ed.) James Strachey. Standard edition, vol. 14, 166–175. The Hogarth Press, London.

Garrity, T. (1969). *The Sensuous Woman*. Lyle Stuart, New York, NY.

Gay, P. (1986). *The Bourgeois Experience: The Tender Passion.* Oxford University Press, New York, NY.

Gaylin, W., & Person, E. (1988). *Passionate Attachments: Thinking about Love.* The Free Press, New York, NY.

Ghent, E. (1990). Masochism, submission, surrender–masochism as a perversion of surrender. *Contemp. Psa.*, 26, 108–136.

Giles, D. (ed.) (1989). combined volume (1991). *Masochism Sacher-Masoch, L. v. Coldness and Cruelty. Venus in Furs.* Zone Books, New York, NY.

Gillespie, W. H. (1956). The general theory of sexual perversion. *IJP*, 37, 396–403.

Glick, R. A., & Meyers, D. (ed.) (1988). *Masochism: Current Psychoanalytic Perspectives.* The Analytic Press, Mahwah, NJ.

Glickhauf-Hughes, C., & Wells, M. (1995). *Treatment of the Masochistic Personality.* Jason Aronson, Lanham, MD.

Goldberg, A. (1995). *The Problem of Perversion: View from Self Psychology.* Yale University Press, New Haven, CT.

Greenacre, P. (1970). The transitional object and the fetish with special reference to the role of illusion. *IJP*, 51, 447–456.

Greenacre, P. (1971). *Emotional Growth.* Chapter 12, pp. 182–198. International Universities Press, Madison, CT.

Harrington, C., Tillotson, D., & Winters, N. C. (eds.) (2022). *Body as Psychoanalytic Object.* Routledge, London & New York, NY.

Hawley, P. H., & Hensley, W. A., IV. (2009). Social dominance and forceful submission fantasies: Feminine pathology or power? *Journal of Sex Research*, 46, 568–585.

Hébert, A., & Weaver, A. (2014). An examination of the personality characteristics associated with BDSM orientations. *The Canadian Journal of Human Sexuality*, 23, 106–115.

Hillier, K. (2019). The impact of childhood trauma and personality on kinkiness in adulthood (Doctoral dissertation, Minneapolis, MN: Walden University).

Hirschfeld, M. (1932). *Sexual Pathology-Being a Study of the Abnormalities of the Sexual Function.* Julian Press, New York, NY. History of erotic literature. https://en.m.wikipedia.org/wiki/Erotic_literature.

Hislop, J. (2001). *Female Sex Offenders.* Issues Press, Ravensdale, WA.

Hite, S. (1976). *The Hite Report: A Nationwide Study of Female Sexuality.* Seven Stories Press, New York, NY.

Holvoet, L., Huys, W., Coppens, V., Seeuws, J., Goethals, K., & Morrens, M. (2017). Fifty Shades of Belgian Gray: The Prevalence of BDSM-Related Fantasies and Activities in the General Population. *The Journal of Sexual Medicine*, 14, 1152–1159.

Hunt, L. (ed.) (1996). *The Invention of Pornography: Obscenity and the Origins of Modernity, 1500–1800.* Zone Books, New York, NY.

Ingram, H. I. (2010). *Sex and Psychodynamic Psychiatry J. Am. Aca. Psa, Dyn. Psy., Special Issue.* The Guilford Press, New York, NY.

James, E. L. (2012). *Fifty Shades of Grey Vintage Books.* Knopf Doubleday Publishing, New York, NY.

Janus, S., Bess, B., & Saltus, C. (1977). *A Sexual Profile of Men in Power.* Prentice-Hall, New Jersey.

Joseph, B. (1971). A clinical contribution to the analysis of a perversion. *IJP*, 52, 441–449.

Joyal, C. C. (2015). Defining "normophilic" and "paraphilic" sexual fantasies in a population-based sample: On the importance of considering subgroups. *Sexual Medicine*, 3, 321–330.

Joyal, C. C., & Carpentier, J. (2017). The prevalence of paraphilic interests and behaviors in the general population: A provincial survey. *Journal of Sex Research*, 54, 161–171.

Joyal, C. C., Cossette, A., & Lapierre, V. (2015). What exactly is an unusual sexual fantasy? *The Journal of Sexual Medicine*, 12, 328–340.

Kahn, M. R. (1969). Role of the collated internal object in perversion formations. *IJP*, 50, 555–565.

Kahn, M. R. (1989). *Alienation in the Perversions*. Marsfield Library, London.

Kaplan, H. S. (1974). *The New Sex Therapy*. Bruner Mazel, New York, NY.

Kaplan, H. S. (1987). *Sexual Aversion, Sexual Phobias, and Panic Disorder*. Bruner-Mazel, New York, NY.

Kaplan, L. J. (1991). *Female Perversions*. Aronson, Lanham, MD.

Karlen, A. (1988). *Threesomes: Studies in Sex, Power, and Intimacy*. Beach Tree Books, William Morrow, New York, NY.

Kernberg, O. F. (1995). *Love Relations: Normality and Pathology*. Yale University Press, New Haven, CT.

Kimberly, C., Williams, A. L., & Creel, S. (2018). Women's introduction to alternative sexual behaviors through erotica and its association with sexual and relationship satisfaction. *Sex Roles*, 78, 119–129.

Kinsey, A. C., & Clyde, E. M. (1948). *Sexual Behavior in the Human Male*. Indiana University Press, Bloomington, IN.

Kinsey, A. C., & Clyde, E. M. (1953). *Sexual Behavior in the Human Female*. WB Saunders, Philadelphia, PA.

Kraft-Ebbing, R. (1894). *Psychpathia Sexualis, Contrary Sexual Instinct* (Tr.) C. G. Chaddoch. 7th revised edition. The FA Davis Co, Philadelphia, PA.

Kraft-Ebbing, R. (1886 [1965]). *Psychopathia Sexualis First unexpurgated edition in English* (Tr.) H. E. Wedeck. GP Putnam's Sons, New York, NY.

Krafft-Ebing, R. (1906). With opportunity for the natural satisfaction of the sexual instinct, every expression of it that does not correspond with the purpose of nature – i.e., propagation – must be regarded as perverse, p. 76.

Kramer, S., & Akhtar, S. (ed.) (1992). *When the Body Speaks: Psychological Meanings in Kinetic Cues*. Aronson, Lanham, MD.

Kronhausen, P., & Kronhausen, E. (1969). *A Study of the Sexual Imagination*. Bell Publishing Co., New York, NY.

Laufer, M. (1964). Ego ideal and pseudo ego ideal in adolescence. *Psychoanalytic Study of the Child*, 19, 196–221.

Laufer, M. (1968). The body image, the function of masturbation, and adolescence, problems of the ownership of the body. *Psychoanal Study Child*, 23, 114–137.

Laufer, M. (1976). The central masturbation fantasy, the final sexual organization, and adolescence. *Psychoanalytic Study of the Child*, 31, 297–316.

Laufer, M. (1981). The psychoanalyst and the adolescent's sexual development. *Psychoanalytic Study of the Child*, 36, 181–191.

Lehmiller, J. J. (2018). *Tell Me What You Want*. De Capo Press, New York, NY.

Lemma, A. (2015). Distinguishing perverse and non-perverse uses of prostitutes. Chapter 10. In Lemma, A. & Lynch, P. *Sexualities*. Routledge, London & New York, NY.

Lemma, A., & Lynch, P. (2015). *Sexualities*. Routledge, London & New York, NY.

Lester, M. (1957). The analysis of an unconscious beating fantasy in a woman. *PsaQ*, 27, 127–137.

Loewenstein, R. M. (1957). A contribution to the psychoanalytic theory of masochism. *IJP*, 39: 443–444.

Lorand, S. L. (ed.), & Balint, M. (assoc. ed.). (1956). *Perversions: Psychodynamics and Therapy*. Random House, New York, NY.

Lowenstein, R. M. (1958). A contribution to the theory of masochism. *IJP*, 39, 443–444.

Lunde, I., Larson, G. K., Fog, E., & Garde, K. (1991). Sexual Desire, Orgasm, and Sexual Fantasies: A Study of 625 Danish Women Born in 1910, 1936, and 1958. *Journal of Sex Education and Therapy* 17(2), 111–115.

Luo, S., & Zhang, X. (2018). Empathy in female submissive BDSM practitioners. *Neuropsychologia*, 116, 44–51.

MacDougal, J. (1985). *Theaters of the Mind: Illusion and Truth on the Psychoanalytic Stage*. Basic Books, New York, NY.

MacDougal, J. (1989). *Theaters of the Body: A Psychoanalytic Approach to Psychosomatic Illness*. WW Norton & Co., New York, NY.

MacDougal, J. (1995). *The Many Faces of Eros*. WW Norton, Inc., New York, NY.

Malloy, J. R. (1992). *The Psychopathic Mind*. Aronson, New York, NY.

Marcus, E. R. (2017). *Psychosis and Near Psychosis: Ego Function, Symbol Structure, Treatment*. Revised third edition. Routledge, Abington-on-Thames.

Marcus, E. R. (2018). Psychoanalytic meta theory: A modern ego psychology view. *Psychodynamic Psychiatry*, 42(2), 220–230.

Marcus, E. R. (2020a). Modern ego psychology and human sexual experience: Fetish, fetish enactments and perversion. *Canadian Journal of Psa*, 28(2), 226–246.

Marcus, E. R. (2020b). Rigid character, a modern ego psychology view. *Canadian Journal of Psa*, 28(2), 208–225.

Marcus, I. M. (1975). *Masturbation: From Infancy to Senescence*. International University Press, Madison, CT.

Masters, W. H., & Johnson, V. E. (1966). *Human Sexual Response*. Bantam Books, Toronto & New York, NY.

May, R. (1980). *Sex & Fantasy: Patterns of Male & Female Development*. WW Norton, New York, NY.

McCarthy, B., & McCarthy, E. (2021). *Contemporary Male Sexuality*. Routledge, Abington-on-Thames.

McWilliams, N. (2011). *Psychoanalytic Diagnosis*. Second edition. The Guilford Press, New York, NY.

Meltzer, D. (1973). *Sexual States of Mind*. Neill Co., Edinburgh.

Meltzer, D. (1974). A theory of sexual perversion. In *Adolescence: Talks in Papers By Donald Meltzer and Martha*, pp. 205–220. (Ed.) M. H. Williams. Karnac Books, London.

Miller, F. (1981). Etiological factors in a case of male perversion. *JAPA*, 41(1), 39–44.

Morganthaler, F. (1988). *Homosexuality, Heterosexuality, Perversion* (Tr.) A. Aebi. Analytic Press, New Jersey.

Nordling, N., Sandnabba, N. K., Santtila, P., & Alison, L. (2006). Differences and similarities between gay and straight individuals involved in the sadomasochistic subculture. *Journal of Homosexuality*, 50, 41–57.

Novick, J., & Novick, K. K. (1996). *Fearful Symmetry: The Development and Treatment of Sadomasochism*. Aronson, Lanham, MD.

Ober, W. B. (1987). *Bottoms Up Souther*. Illinois University Press, Champaign, IL.

Offit, A. K. (1995). *Night Thoughts-Reflections of a Sex Therapist*. Revised edition. Aronson, New York, NY.

Ostow, M. (ed.) (1974). *Sexual Deviation*. New York Times Book Co., New York, NY.

Parsons, M. (2000). Discovering what freud discovered: Sexuality and perversion one hundred years on. *IJP*, 81, 37–51.

Person, E. S. (1988). *Dreams of Love and Fateful Encounters: The Power of Romantic Attachments.* WW Norton, New York, NY.

Person, E. S. (1995). *By Force of Fantasy Basic Books.* USA Perversion: PEP web. www.pep-web. org.ezproxy.cul.columbia.edu/search.php?fulltext1=perversion&zone1=article&zone2= paragraphs&viewperiod=week&sort=author%2Ca&pagenum=1

Person, E. S. (1999). *The Sexual Century.* Yale University Press, New Haven, CN.

Racker, H. (1968). *Transference and Countertransference.* International Universities Press, Inc., New York, NY.

Reagé, P. (1954). *Story of O.* Jean-Jacque Pauvert, Paris.

Rehor, J. E. (2015). Sensual, erotic, and sexual behaviors of women from the "kink" community. *Archives of Sexual Behavior*, 44, 825–836.

Reich, A. (1953). Narcissistic object choice in women. *J Am PsychoanalAssoc*, 1, 22–44.

Richards, A., & Tyson, P. (1996). The Psychology of Women. *JAPA*, 44(Suppl.). International Universities Press, USA.

Roiphe, H., & Galenson, E. (1987). Pre-oedipal roots of perversion. *Psa. Inq.*, 7(3), 415–430.

Rothstein, A. (1991). Sadomasochism in the neuroses conceived of as a pathological compromise formation. *Journal of the American Psychoanalytic Association*, 39, 363–375.

Saketopoulou, A. (2014). To suffer pleasure: The shattering of the ego as the psychic labor of perverse sexuality. *Studies in Gender and Sexuality*, 15(4), 254–264.

Saketopoulou, A. (2015). On sexual perversion's capacity to act as a portal to psychic states that have evaded representation. Chapter 12 in Lemma, A. & Lynch, P. *Sexualities.* Routledge, London & New York, NY.

Sanchez, D. T., Kiefer, A. K., & Ybarra, O. (2006). Sexual submissiveness in women: Costs for sexual autonomy and arousal. *Personality and Social Psychology Bulletin*, 32, 512–524.

Scruton, R. (1986). *Sexual Desire: A Moral Philosophy of the Erotic.* The Free Press, New York, NY.

Shad-Somers, S. P. (1982). *Sadomasochism: Etiology and Treatment.* Human Sciences Press, New York, NY.

Shaw, D. (2012). *Traumatic Narcissism: Relational Systems of Subjugation (Relational Perspectives.* Book Series, 1st edition. Routledge, Abington-on-Thames.

Shengold, L. (1988). *Halo in the Sky: Observations on Anality and Defense.* Yale University Press, New Haven, CN.

Shtekel, W. (1929). *Sadism and Masochism.* English version by Louise Brink, PhD. Liveright Publishing Co., New York, NY.

Shulman, J. L., & Home, S. G. (2006). Guilty or not? A path model of women's sexual force fantasies. *Journal of Sex Research*, 43(4), 368–377.

Simmel, G. (1984). *On Women: Sexuality, and Love* (Tr.) G. Oakes. Yale Press, New Haven, CT.

Smith, M. D. (ed.) (2001). *Sex Without Consent.* New York University Press, New York, NY.

Steckel, W. (1930). *Sexual Aberrations: The Phenomenon of Fetishism in Relation to Sex*, vol. 1-vol 2. Authorized English version Dr. S. Parker. Liveright Publishing, New York, NY.

Stimson, C. R., & Person, E. S. (eds.) (1980). *Women: Sex and Sexuality.* The University of Chicago Press, Chicago.

Stoler, R. (1979). *Sexual Excitement.* BPC Weatons, Ltd., GT Britain.

Theweleit, K. (1989). *Male Fantasies*, vol. 1 & 2. University of Minnesota Press, Minneapolis, MN.

Tomassilli, J. C., Golub, S. A., Bimbi, D. S., & Parsons, J. T. (2009). Behind closed doors: An exploration of kinky sexual behaviors in urban lesbian and bisexual women. *Journal of Sex Research*, 46, 438–444.

Volkan, V. D. (1981). *Linking Objects and Linking Phenomena: A Study of the Forms, Symptoms, Metapsychology and Therapy of Complicated Mourning*. International Universities Press, New York, NY.

Watts, A. L., Nagel, M. G., Latzman, R. D., & Lilienfeld, S. O. (2019). Personality disorder features and paraphilic interests among undergraduates: Differential relations and potential antecedents. *Journal of Personality Disorders*, 33, 22–32.

Weininger, O. (1907). *Sex & Character Sixth Edition Authorized Translation*. GP Putnam & Sons, New York, NY.

Williams, A. H. (1957). Perversions, psychodynamics and therapy. *IJP*, 38, 432–442.

Williams, D. (2006). Different (Painful) strokes for different folks: A general overview of sexual sadomasochism (SM) and its diversity. *Sexual Addiction & Compulsivity*, 13, 333–346.

Williams, D., Prior, E. E., Alvarado, T., Thomas, J. N., & Christensen, M. C. (2016). Is bondage and discipline, dominance and submission, and sadomasochism recreational leisure? A descriptive exploratory investigation. *The Journal of Sexual Medicine*, 13, 1091–1094.

Williams, K. M., Cooper, B. S., Howell, T. M., Yuille, J. C., & Paulhus, D. L. (2009). Inferring sexually deviant behavior from corresponding fantasies: The role of personality and pornography consumption. *Criminal Justice and Behavior*, 36, 198–222.

Winnicott, D. W. (1971). *Playing and Reality*. Tavistock Publishing, Ltd., London.

Wismeijer, A. A., & Van Assen, M. A. (2013). Psychological characteristics of BDSM practitioners. *The Journal of Sexual Medicine*, 10(8), 1943–1952.

Yost, M. R., & Hunter, L. (2012). BDSM practitioners' understandings of their initial attraction to BDSM sexuality: Essentialist and constructionist narratives. *Psychology & Sexuality*, 3, 244–259.

Zavitzianos, G. (1982). The perversion of fetishism and women. *PsaQ*, 51, 405–425.

Zurbriggen, E. L., & Yost, M. R. (2004). Power, desire, and pleasure in sexual fantasies. *Journal of Sex Research*, 41, 288–300.

Index

abandonment, cause 44
acute trauma 42, 105; adaptations 116
acute traumatic event 44
Adam/Eve, Garden exit (reason) 90
adaptation, counseling problem 88–89
addiction: label 62; object, attachment 59;
  reinforcement 62
addictive attachment 63; type 62
addictive objects, unavailability 62
adolescent intellectual development, lust
  (impact) 45
adolescent physical changes, lust (impact)
  45
adrenarche 32, 45
adult sharing, physical experience 57
affect: concept, experience 17; experience
  5, 10; intensity, condensed experience
  (relationship) 20; lust affect 19–21;
  storms, increase 105
affect ideas 3; core affect idea 37
affect meaning 3; maker 4
affect representations 4; focus 2
aggression 84; management 96; object,
  combination 34; penis, hardness 98;
  purpose 102
ambition, inhibition 60
ambivalence, usage 90
analog information system, providing
  10
analyst, desire (countertransference
  difficulty) 123
analytic method, usage 70
anatomy, part (valuation) 59–60
anger, trigger 63
angry object, attraction 62–63
anxiety: cause 44; containment 77;
  defenses 92; feeling 100; plot
  motivations 70; trigger 40

arousal 68; analyst material, evocation
  121; cause, lust (impact) 19–20;
  conscious component 108–109;
  details 70; ego state 22; excitement,
  intensity 22; fantasy, impact 23; fantasy,
  meeting/joining 72; impact 50;
  initiation 109–110
arousal cycle 21–22, 69, 103; attachment,
  emotional meaning/satisfaction 23;
  progression 70; steps 21, 36; story 22
arousal nodes 70; inhibition 36
assertion, penis (hardness) 98
attachment 56; anxieties 61; bond,
  ownership type 101; commitment
  problems 59; diversionary arrangements
  91; emotional attachment trauma
  history/difficulties 51; emotional
  meaning/satisfaction 23; example
  60–67; fear 47; history 69; loving
  attachment 66; meta-themes 70;
  neurotic forms 58; permanence issues
  58; possibility 61; prevention,
  ambivalence (usage) 90; problems,
  impact 89; problems, representation 67;
  relationships 59; romantic/romanticized
  attachment 28; sensory manifestation
  memories 57; sociopath betrayal 67;
  style 32–33; unavailable object,
  attachment 59
attention deficit disorder 104
attitude, treatment 121
avoidance (trigger), guilt/shame (impact)
  28

betrayal, fear 47
blow job, enjoyment/meaning 64
body: ego 5; emotional reactions 14;
  fetishized use 64–65; love 34, 58;

Lightning Source UK Ltd.
Milton Keynes UK
UKHW020832051022
409949UK00016B/316